MUSIC
TECHNOLOGY
FROM SCRATCH

Mortimer Rhind-Tutt

R· RHINEGOLD
EDUCATION

ww.   .co.uk

Music Study Guides

GCSE, AS and A2 Music Study Guides (AQA, Edexcel and OCR)
GCSE, AS and A2 Music Listening Tests (AQA, Edexcel and OCR)
AS/A2 Music Technology Study Guide (Edexcel)
AS/A2 Music Technology Listening Tests (Edexcel)
Revision Guides for GCSE (AQA, Edexcel and OCR), AS and A2 Music (AQA and Edexcel)

Also available from Rhinegold Education

Key Stage 3 Listening Tests: Book 1 and Book 2
AS and A2 Music Harmony Workbooks
GCSE and AS Music Composition Workbooks
GCSE and AS Music Literacy Workbooks
Romanticism in Focus, Baroque Music in Focus, Film Music in Focus, Modernism in Focus,
The Immaculate Collection in Focus, *Who's Next* in Focus, *Batman* in Focus, *Goldfinger* in Focus,
Musicals in Focus
Rhinegold Dictionary of Music in Sound

Other Rhinegold Study Guides

Rhinegold publishes resources for candidates studying Drama and Theatre Studies.

First published 2009 in Great Britain by
Rhinegold Education
14-15 Berners Street,
London W1T 3LJ, UK.
www.rhinegoldeducation.co.uk

Music Technology from Scratch
British Library Cataloguing in Publication Data.
A catalogue record for this book is available from the British Library.
Order No. RHG318
ISBN 978-1-906178-86-4

Exclusive Distributors:
Music Sales Limited
Distribution Centre, Newmarket Road,
Bury St Edmunds, Suffolk IP33 3YB, UK.

Music Sales Pty Limited
20 Resolution Drive, Caringbah, NSW 2229, Australia.

Printed in the EU.

CONTENTS

INTRODUCTION

Music technology has changed out of all recognition in the recent past. The digital revolution and developments in the global economy have opened the worlds of recording and sound manipulation to everyone. It is now routine to record a track at home and release it worldwide. Sound can be edited and mixed for video, theatre productions, websites or any number of other activities using equipment that would have been unaffordable just a few years ago. However, as with desktop publishing and digital photography, the availability of technology does not automatically bring with it the skills, knowledge and understanding of a whole specialist industry. This book sets out to demystify the process involved and enable novices in the field to approach music technology with confidence.

Section 1 examines the basics – the equipment you are likely to use, the background to its development and the underlying theory. The book is designed to be used while experimenting with some of this equipment. If you are teaching in school or following an educational course hopefully everything described in Section 1 will be available to you. If not, this section will help you to decide which equipment you need and to understand how to get the most from it. The best way to understand music technology is to use it and each chapter ends with some suggestions for experimentation.

Section 2 outlines the processes of recording, mixing and mastering as well as MIDI sequencing and some aspects of composing and arranging. It builds on the basics explained in Section 1 and there are coloured links between chapters in both sections. A glossary explains terms highlighted in bold in the text (and others) and a comprehensive index enables readers to search for specific topics.

Computers play a big part in the world of music technology today. Software creates 'virtual' versions of real equipment. Section 1 encourages you to find and experiment with that equipment so that you can fully understand the processes that happen in the software equivalents. In Section 2 most of the processes described are from the point of view of a computer user, but keep in mind that multi-track recorders and other hardware still offer an important and sometimes preferable alternative.

This book is intended as a 'primer' – there is much more detail to be discovered from further study and experience. I hope that it will be helpful to anyone studying music technology, to teachers looking to get started with the subject and anyone wanting to enhance their skills and knowledge.

Mortimer Rhind-Tutt

CHAPTER 1
THE BASICS

HEARING SOUND

▶ HOW DO WE HEAR SOUND?

Our ears hear sound by reacting to changes in the pressure of the air around us. These air pressure changes are turned into chemical and electrical signals which the brain can understand. Ears are very sensitive and can cope with a wide range of sound levels – although they can be damaged by too much sound pressure.

▶ HOW DOES SOUND TRAVEL?

A simple way of understanding air pressure changes is to think of them as **waves** in the air between whatever is making the sound and whoever is hearing it.

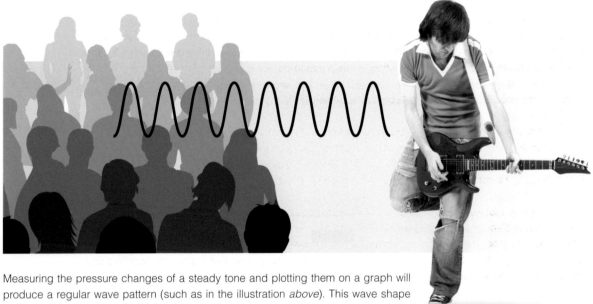

Measuring the pressure changes of a steady tone and plotting them on a graph will produce a regular wave pattern (such as in the illustration *above*). This wave shape is what we see on screen in our music software when we view the equivalent audio signal or digital waveform.

▶ PITCH

We understand sounds to be high or low and call this pitch. With musical notes, though, we are more specific than just high or low – we label the notes with the letters A to G (as on a keyboard) or with the **frequency** of the wave.

▶ VOLUME

We also hear changes in the volume of sounds, which we call 'loud' or 'soft'. How our brains make this judgement is affected by a variety of properties of the sound but, to keep things simple, the volume of a sound wave is usually known as its **amplitude**.

▶ HOW IS SOUND USED IN MUSIC TECHNOLOGY?

To make use of sound for performing and recording, sound waves are turned into electrical signals. These signals travel through wires (such as a microphone lead), and eventually, using a **loudspeaker** or a **monitor**, are turned back into sound waves in the air again. However amazing our technology becomes, these are the basic steps we need to be able to make.

Sound waves in the air are invisible, but we can compare them with other waves such as those in the sea.

If you stand in the sea, waves continually pass you by and you will notice that they have high points (**peaks**) and low points (**troughs**).

Frequency simply means how often something happens. So the frequency of a wave in the sea is the number of peaks to pass you in a certain amount of time – for example, 30 per minute.

▶ CYCLES

Each time a wave reaches you, the sea water will have been through some changes including a peak, a trough and moments when the water is flat. The whole sequence between any two similar points is called a **cycle**, so a wave could have a frequency of 30 cycles per minute.

A WAVE IN THE SEA

Wave travelling towards land

1 CYCLE   FLAT SEA PEAK   TROUGH

FACT
Frequency is measured in **Hertz**, named after the scientist Heinrich Hertz. One cycle per second is called 1 Hertz (or 1 Hz).

▶ PITCH AND FREQUENCY

Sound waves in the air are much faster than waves in the sea, and have a much higher frequency.

The frequency of a sound wave determines its pitch. The higher the frequency, the higher the pitch.

The note A in the middle of a piano has a frequency of 440 Hz, meaning that the air is vibrating 440 times per second.

As the frequency goes up, so does the pitch of a note. There is a neat relationship here, as every time a frequency doubles we hear a note one octave higher – so the next A up on the keyboard has a frequency of 880 Hz.

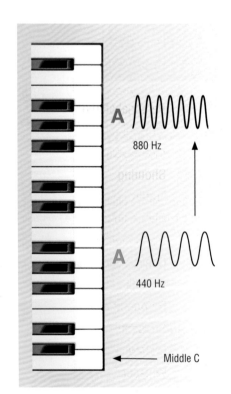

A 880 Hz

A 440 Hz

Middle C

FACT
The human ear can hear sounds from about 20 Hz to about 20,000 Hz (20 kilohertz, or kHz), although the higher frequencies become less clear with age. Some animals can hear much higher frequencies than us.

AMPLITUDE

Sometimes the sea can be really calm and almost flat – the waves then have a **low amplitude**. When they swell up and the peaks become taller, they have a **high amplitude**.

The amplitude of a sound wave affects its volume.

A sound wave with a low amplitude has a low volume (i.e. a soft sound).

A sound wave with a higher amplitude has a higher volume (i.e. a louder sound). This is where the familiar word 'amplifier' comes from – a piece of electronic equipment that boosts the signal of a microphone, sound system or instrument.

LOW AMPLITUDE

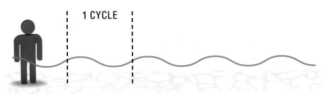

1 CYCLE

HIGH AMPLITUDE

1 CYCLE

Both waves have the same frequency but one is stronger.

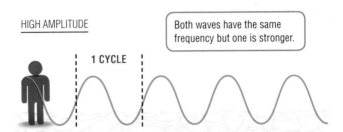

dB	Sound
140	Jet plane
130	Fireworks
120	Rock concert
	Chainsaw
110	Personal stereo
100	Timpani
90	Motorcycle
	Shouting
80	Traffic
70	Phone ringing
60	Piano practice
	Conversation
50	Rainfall
40	Refrigerator
30	Birdsong
20	Library
	Whisper
10	Breathing
0	Silence

▶ **VOLUME MEASUREMENT**

The measurement of volume is usually shown on a scale of **decibels**. Each decibel (dB) is one tenth of a Bel, named after Alexander Graham Bell, an early pioneer of the telephone.

Decibels compare sound levels rather than actually measuring them. As the scale goes up, the changes become much more noticeable. For example the difference between 70 dB and 80 dB is much greater than than the difference between 10 dB and 20 dB.

If you listen to sounds above about 85 dB for any length of time, damage to your ears will result. At about 130 dB sound levels start to be painful and damage to your hearing is likely without protection. This is worth keeping in mind when working in studios with drums and amplified music.

SOUND AND ELECTRICITY

▶ FROM SOUND TO ELECTRICITY

We are all familiar with the idea of singing into a microphone and listening to loudspeakers, and in this section we are going to look at how these work. You don't need to understand all the science and maths involved to grasp music technology, but it helps to have some idea of the basic principles.

When a sound is made, the air vibrates and creates a wave. To imitate this effect with electricity, the strength (voltage) of an electrical signal must change (go up and down in strength) in the same way as the sound wave is changing.

The telephone, invented in the 1870s, was probably the first example of sound technology. Many years of experimenting were needed to make it work.

Some of the first telephones were based on the idea of **electro-magnetism**, and this is still the way in which most loudspeakers and some microphones work.

▶ ELECTROMAGNETISM

An electromagnet is created whenever electricity passes through a wire. The wire becomes magnetic and will attract metal objects towards it. This effect becomes more obvious when the wire is coiled up and even stronger if it is wound around some metal.

The opposite also happens – magnetism can generate electricity. If a magnet is moved across a wire then electricity starts to flow in the wire. Again, the effect is much stronger if the wire is coiled and wound around a metal shape of some kind.

On the opposite page, you can follow how, using electromagnetism, a microphone converts a sound wave into an electrical signal and how a loudspeaker then converts that signal back into a sound wave.

SOUND TO ELECTRICITY AND BACK AGAIN

▶ INSIDE A MICROPHONE – HOW SOUND IS CONVERTED INTO ELECTRICITY

Sound waves in the air ❶ hit a thin metal plate called a **diaphragm** ❷ inside the microphone.

This diaphragm is attached to a cylinder with a coil of wire wrapped around it ❸, and when it is moved by sound waves it makes the coil move rapidly across the field of a magnet.

The magnetic field creates a small electrical voltage in the coil ❹ which is continually changing as the sound wave changes. We usually call this flow of electricity a signal, or audio (sound) signal ❺.

In **Chapter 4** we will look at microphones in more detail.

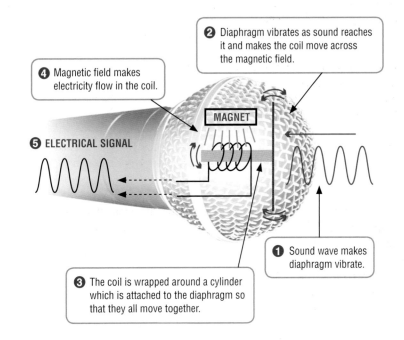

❷ Diaphragm vibrates as sound reaches it and makes the coil move across the magnetic field.

❹ Magnetic field makes electricity flow in the coil.

MAGNET

❺ ELECTRICAL SIGNAL

❶ Sound wave makes diaphragm vibrate.

❸ The coil is wrapped around a cylinder which is attached to the diaphragm so that they all move together.

▶ INSIDE A LOUDSPEAKER – HOW ELECTRICITY IS CONVERTED INTO SOUND

In a loudspeaker, an electrical audio signal ❶ is fed to the wires of a coil of wire surrounding a cylinder ❷. This makes the coil magnetic.

The amount of magnetism created varies rapidly as the electrical signal changes, and this makes the coil vibrate as it is attracted to a fixed magnet nearby.

The cylinder is attached to a cone made of card (or some other flexible material) ❸. As the coil vibrates it makes the cone move too, causing the air around it to vibrate and creating a sound wave ❹.

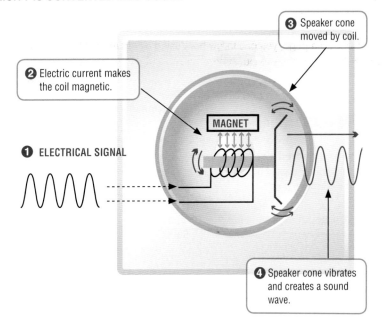

❸ Speaker cone moved by coil.

❷ Electric current makes the coil magnetic.

MAGNET

❶ ELECTRICAL SIGNAL

❹ Speaker cone vibrates and creates a sound wave.

AMPLIFYING SOUND

These three diagrams show how a sound wave can be converted into an electrical signal and back to a sound wave.

❶ DOWN THE WIRE

If a microphone turns sound into electricity and a loudspeaker turns electricity into sound, can we just join them together and send a sound along a wire?

SIGNAL STRENGTH
The voltage from a microphone is extremely small – measured in thousandths of a volt. It isn't strong enough to produce a sound we could hear easily from a loudspeaker.

| SOUND WAVE | MICROPHONE | AUDIO SIGNAL | LOUDSPEAKER | SOUND WAVE? |

❷ MAKING YOURSELF HEARD

To be of any use, the tiny electrical signal from a microphone needs to be made larger – amplified. So you need to plug a microphone into the input of an **amplifier** and then connect a loudspeaker to the output of the amplifier.

ELECTRONICS
In most modern amplifiers **transistors** are used. These are able to take a small voltage and change it into a larger one which is strong enough to make a healthy sound from a loudspeaker.

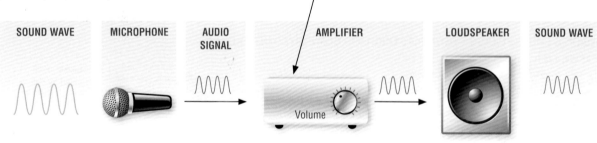

| SOUND WAVE | MICROPHONE | AUDIO SIGNAL | AMPLIFIER | LOUDSPEAKER | SOUND WAVE |

Volume

❸ POWERED MONITORS

Sometimes a loudspeaker and amplifier are combined into one piece of equipment. These are known as **powered monitors** (or sometimes just **monitors**). They range in size from tiny desktop computer speakers to huge units that can fill a hall or stadium with sound.

POWER
When you use an amplifier it will usually say on the case how much power it can produce. This is measured in **watts** (named after James Watt who developed the steam engine). A small amplifier will produce less than one watt and the largest over a thousand.

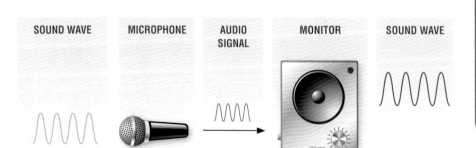

| SOUND WAVE | MICROPHONE | AUDIO SIGNAL | MONITOR | SOUND WAVE |

Volume

MONO AND STEREO

So far we've looked at the idea of sound going into a microphone, becoming an electrical signal, being amplified and then coming back out of a loudspeaker.

If sound is being played through only one loudspeaker then it is described as 'monaural' – usually shortened to **mono**. A guitar amplifier is a good example of mono sound – one guitar plugs in and is played through one speaker.

Almost all equipment we use these days to listen to music or speech is 'stereophonic' – abbreviated to **stereo**. This has two loudspeakers which give us a sense of left and right, an effect which is missing with mono sound. Most televisions, CD players, car sound systems and personal music players have two speakers or earphones.

▶ DOUBLING UP

Having two loudspeakers means that, to make a sound louder, you will need two amplifiers. In fact, any part of the circuitry in stereo equipment will need to be doubled up. Of course, we don't usually have a separate box of tricks for each side – the electronic circuits are duplicated on their boards, and two of everything is fitted into the same casing. The two circuits which run through a stereo amplifier are called the left and right channels.

▶ PANNING

When a sound is sent to a stereo amplifier, the **pan** control divides its signal between the left and right channels. If an equal amount of signal goes to both channels, the sound seems to be in the centre – it can then be shifted either left or right by sending more signal to one of the loudspeakers than the other. For more on **controls**, see page 134.

The sound waves from each speaker reach the audience's ears at different times. This, combined with the relative strength of a sound on each side, gives the illusion of left-to-right positioning.

ANALOG SOUND

▶ WHAT IS ANALOG SOUND?

A microphone turns sound into an electrical signal. The changes in strength and pitch of the sound are reflected in the strength and frequency of the electrical signal, thus making a comparison or 'analogy' between them.

Common formats for analog recording are **vinyl records** and **magnetic tape**.

▶ FEATURES OF ANALOG SOUND

- The changes in both sound and electrical signal are continuous
- If the sound becomes louder, the electrical signal becomes stronger
- If the pitch of the sound goes up, the frequency of change from positive to negative electricity becomes faster.

During playback, the continuous variation in electrical strength and frequency is changed back into sound waves by a loudspeaker.

Changes in the signal are continuous

▶ OTHER EXAMPLES OF ANALOG

In an analog thermometer, the temperature is shown by the mercury. If the mercury is high, the temperature is high, and changes are continuous. The position of the mercury line is analagous to the temperature.

Analog sound represents sound waves as electrical signals. Changes in pressure travelling through the air (the sound wave) are represented as changes in the strength and frequency of an electrical signal travelling along wires.

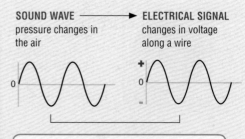

SOUND WAVE ⟶ ELECTRICAL SIGNAL
pressure changes in the air — changes in voltage along a wire

At each point in the cycle, the electrical signal is comparable with the sound wave.

Many devices in daily use represent the world in an analog form, such as a clock face, thermometer or a speedometer that has a needle moving across a dial. They form a 'picture' of the information we need to read.

▶ BACK AND FORTH

Once sound has been turned into an electrical signal, it can be amplified or changed. If the electrical signal is increased or distorted, those changes will be heard when it is turned back to a sound wave. Guitar amplifiers sometimes add distortion to sounds, and occasionally have reverb effects built in. Effects are generally quite difficult to achieve with analog signals alone, needing either complex electronic circuits or sometimes a mechanical process to alter the signal as well.

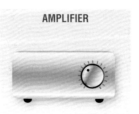

MIC   AUDIO SIGNAL   AMPLIFIER   DISTORTED ANALOG SIGNAL   LOUDSPEAKER

The electrical signal is amplified and distorted as it passes through the amplifier.

DIGITAL SOUND

▶ WHAT IS DIGITAL SOUND?

Instead of comparing the characteristics of sound to something else, digital sound measures it and represents it as numbers. By taking a measurement at regular intervals of pitch, volume, timbre and any other useful information, a mathematical description is built up of the sound. Each measurement is called a **sample**. This is a two stage process – the sound becomes an electrical (analog) signal first and is then 'sampled'.

Common formats for digital recording are **CD**, **DVD**, **DAT**, **MiniDisc** and **MP3**.

▶ FEATURES OF DIGITAL SOUND

- The changes in the samples are not continuous but are in discrete steps
- As volume or pitch changes, the numerical information changes
- If a sound was only sampled a few times per second, the playback quality would be poor with lots of gaps, rather like the sound when you 'fast forward' through a CD or DVD.

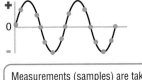

Measurements (samples) are taken at intervals along the waveform

The number of samples per second is known as the **sample rate** and as it increases, we cease to notice the tiny chunks of sound. The amount of information measured in each sample is known as the **bit depth** or **resolution**. Digital sound for CD quality has 44,100 samples per second with a 16 bit resolution.

▶ OTHER EXAMPLES OF DIGITAL

A digital thermometer 'samples' the temperature around it at regular intervals, so changes are not continuous. If the sampling was only once per hour, it would not be very helpful. Once per second would give a useful result. Digital devices do not form a direct 'picture' of information, but instead store a mathematical representation of it which can be displayed on a screen.

Each time the waveform of a sound is sampled, information about it is measured as a number, which can be stored. For playback, the numbers can be used to calculate the waveform again.

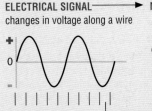

ELECTRICAL SIGNAL → NUMERICAL SAMPLES
changes in voltage along a wire

```
100101011001011
110101011001111
000101011101010
101101011001011
100111011001011
101101110001010
100101001001011
101101011001010
111101011011011
100101011001110
```

At discrete points in the cycle, information about the electrical signal is analysed as a number.

▶ BACK AND FORTH

An analog-to-digital (shortened to A/D) converter analyses the signal and produces the numerical information about the sound. This is done using a microprocessor (similar to a computer 'chip'). While the sound is in digital format, it can be changed by altering the numerical information. Distortion, reverb, delay and all popular effects can be added inside the processing circuit. A digital-to-analog converter (D/A) reprocesses the numbers back into an electrical signal, which can be played back through a loudspeaker.

MIC	AUDIO SIGNAL	A/D CONVERTER	DIGITAL FX UNIT	D/A CONVERTER	DISTORTED ANALOG SIGNAL	LOUDSPEAKER

The digital information is altered as it passes through the effects unit – the resulting audio signal is therefore different too.

▶VINYL RECORDS

To make a vinyl record, a groove is cut into the vinyl disc by an electromagnetic cutter that vibrates as the audio signal passes through it. The groove varies as the music changes in pitch and volume. For stereo sound, a v-shaped groove has the left channel cut into one side and the right channel cut into the other. The groove follows a spiral pattern starting on the edge and working inwards. The groove is 'analogous' to the audio signal, meaning that it changes in a similar way.

CROSS-SECTION VIEW OF A GROOVE IN THE VINYL

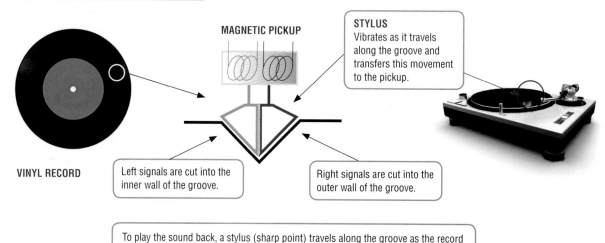

MAGNETIC PICKUP

STYLUS
Vibrates as it travels along the groove and transfers this movement to the pickup.

VINYL RECORD

Left signals are cut into the inner wall of the groove.

Right signals are cut into the outer wall of the groove.

To play the sound back, a stylus (sharp point) travels along the groove as the record spins. The vibration of the stylus in the groove makes a coil move and generates a small signal (in the same way as a microphone does), which can then be amplified. For stereo sound a double stylus/pickup is needed.

Until the 1980s, vinyl records were the main medium for distributing 'Hi Fidelity' (high quality) music. Long playing records (LPs) had several songs on each side and later became known as 'albums'. Smaller records (singles) could have one song on each side. Early gramophones played back the sound mechanically, by picking up the vibrations of the stylus in the groove and transferring them to a 'horn' which in its turn made the air vibrate to create sound. These were replaced by record players with electrical pickups whose signals could then be amplified. The stereo vinyl record arrived in the late 1950s, adding greatly to the enjoyment of listening, and this became the common format from the 1960s onwards.

▶LIMITATIONS

- Noise can be a problem with vinyl records – the groove and stylus can become worn and any dust or dirt affects the playback of the sound
- The disc itself can warp – if it is not truly flat then the edges move up and down as it spins and the sound varies, producing an effect known as 'wow and flutter'.

Vinyl enthusiasts look after their records carefully. A lot of cleaning is needed, and very expensive and stable turntables have been developed for the best possible playback.

FACT
If you listen to tracks from the beginning of the 1950s or earlier, you will hear the noise and frequency range limitations of the recording methods of the times.
Louis Armstrong and Elvis Presley are two artists with long recording careers.
A comparison of their earlier and later work clearly shows the improvements in sound technology.

DIGITAL RECORDING

Instead of directly representing sound as a groove or changing magnetic field, digital recording simply stores the numerical information about the sound. The method of storage can vary – it can be a disc, a computer file or a personal media player. Any differences in sound quality that occur when the file is played on different devices will come from the digital-to-analog conversion circuits and the amplifier circuitry in the device you are using.

▶CD RECORDING

It's easy to put a blank CD into a computer and to 'burn' a disc – but what actually happens when we do this?

The numbers in a digital sound file are all either 0 or 1. This is called 'binary code'. The 0s and 1s are grouped together to make much larger numbers which a computer processor can decode. To store the numbers on a disc, a laser light burns a small mark (called a 'pit') into the surface every time there is a 0 and leaves a blank ('land') wherever there is a 1. These markings follow a spiral pattern starting from the centre and working outwards.

▶CD PLAYBACK

To play the sound back, a less powerful laser shines onto the disc and is reflected back to a detector. The reflection is different when the light bounces off a pit and so the detector recognises a '0'. A '1' is detected when it bounces off the flat, or lighter land. This means that the numbers can be read from the disc and then converted back to an audio signal by a processor similar to that in a computer.

▶COMPUTERS, PLAYERS AND DIGITAL SOUND

Most sound recording and editing now involves computers. Digital sound is stored as files on a hard drive or other memory system. Digital sound files are stored in miniature players, phones, answering machines and a host of other devices.

FACT
If the spiral series of markings on a CD was unwound to a straight line, it would be 5km long.

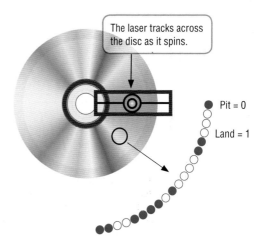

The laser tracks across the disc as it spins.

Pit = 0
Land = 1

ANALOG AND DIGITAL

In the 1980s, the development of digital recording was so fast that the CD replaced vinyl records and tape as the medium of choice in a matter of a few years. Digital recording is virtually noise-free, and every disc is an exact copy of the master recording. With tape and vinyl, the copying process gradually introduces imperfections which build up as it is repeated.

For some people, though, digitally processed sound is too clean and clinical. Analog recordings have a perceived warmth and richness which some producers seek out, rebuilding old equipment and even running digital recordings onto tape and back again to capture the 'sound'.

All recordings have an analog stage. With the availability and affordability of modern equipment it is possible to use a mixture of analog and digital equipment in accordance with your own preferences.

From the late 1940s, tape recorders developed rapidly and became central to the recording of music and sound for broadcast. Large tape machines such as the one pictured are known as 'reel-to-reel'. As the tape is moved between reels by the 'transport' mechanism, it is pressed against tape heads which record, erase or play back the sound.

A tape recorder was used to make the master recordings and for distribution these were transferred to vinyl records. Tape could be edited and re-used introducing a new level of flexibility to the recording process. Earlier in the 20th century, recordings were made directly to vinyl records, wax or tin foil cylinders in one take. Sometimes the musicians were asked to play faster so that the piece would fit onto the recording medium!

By the end of the 1950s, stereo tape machines were available and costs had come down to the point where home taping was practical, although the machines were still very large.

▶ HOW DOES IT WORK?

Tape is coated in stripes of material that 'remembers' magnetic changes applied to it by the tape head. The head has a coil inside it which is connected to the electrical signal from the recorder – this creates a changing magnetic field which affects the material on the tape.

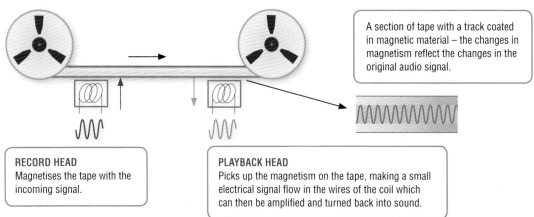

A section of tape with a track coated in magnetic material – the changes in magnetism reflect the changes in the original audio signal.

RECORD HEAD
Magnetises the tape with the incoming signal.

PLAYBACK HEAD
Picks up the magnetism on the tape, making a small electrical signal flow in the wires of the coil which can then be amplified and turned back into sound.

▶ CASSETTE TAPE

In the 1970s, small cassette tape became a popular means of distribution and a serious competitor to vinyl. One great advantage of cassette tape was that you could copy your favourite songs to make a 'mix tape'. Very small players became possible, and the Sony Walkman started the personal media player revolution which continues with the digital MP3 players of today.

▶ LIMITATIONS

- All tape recordings include some 'hiss' – the noise caused by background electrical and magnetic activity on the tape itself
- Tapes are also liable to stretch and break.

Tape recording machines became very sophisticated during the 1970s and 1980s, enabling synchronised multi-track recording at a very high quality. Although tape is still used by some, during the 1990s computer-based digital recording took over the recording, mixing and mastering functions of tape in most studios.

MULTI-TRACK RECORDING

▶BEYOND STEREO

As we saw on page 11, two channels of sound will give us a stereo effect – left and right. For a long time this was the limit of recording technology. Performances had to be recorded 'live', with only one chance to balance and pan the sounds. Microphones would be set some distance away, to capture the whole performance.

The earliest multi-track recording equipment was developed in the late 1940s by Les Paul, also famous for his guitars. The technology progressed slowly, though, and it was not until the early 1960s that it was widely used.

Stereo tape has two 'tracks' of magnetic material which move across the tape heads:

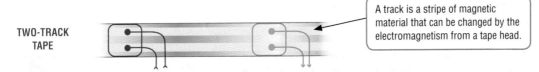

TWO-TRACK TAPE

A track is a stripe of magnetic material that can be changed by the electromagnetism from a tape head.

The challenge early on was to fit more tracks onto one reel of tape. Two became three, and later standardised at four tracks for some time. As one track plays back it is possible to record onto another – a process known as overdubbing.

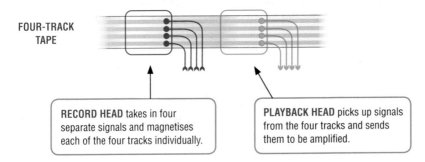

FOUR-TRACK TAPE

RECORD HEAD takes in four separate signals and magnetises each of the four tracks individually.

PLAYBACK HEAD picks up signals from the four tracks and sends them to be amplified.

This step-by-step recording technique also allows for close positioning of microphones. The idea of a track of sound is now used to represent recordings visually on a computer screen.

During the 1960s, eight-track recording become possible, rising to 16 and even 24 as time went on. This involved very expensive and complex machines that needed careful handling, and could only be used in recording studios run on large budgets.

Among the first commercial artists to record using four- or eight-track machines were the Beatles and the Beach Boys during the 1960s. The Album 'Pet Sounds' (1966) by the Beach Boys cleverly uses eight-track technology to individually record and mix the voices.

▶EDITING

Early recording technology was primitive and inflexible. It was necessary to record a performance in one take, and there was no possibility of correcting anything afterwards. Tape offered the possibility of editing. A performance could be recorded more than once and the best sections could be literally cut and spliced together. The angled cut creates a crossfade – as the join passes the tape head, the proportion of each section playing changes, avoiding a sudden change.

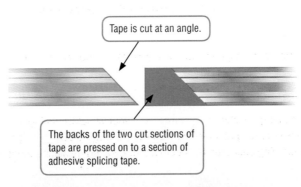

Tape is cut at an angle.

The backs of the two cut sections of tape are pressed on to a section of adhesive splicing tape.

PROJECTS AND SUGGESTIONS

▶ TAPE AND BEYOND

You may be wondering what the point is of looking at tape, vinyl and other recording formats that you may never have used or even seen.

The main reason is that all audio technology that has ever been invented has left some kind of legacy. The language and ideas used in modern digital work often come from older technology. We still cut, splice and crossfade. We still use tracks and channels and even the labelling of sockets and controls on equipment still sometimes refers to 'tape'.

Apart from this, some understanding of basic science, electronics and technology will enable you to produce better recordings in the same way that understanding your car will make you a better driver.

Understanding of ideas such as sound waves and electronics can happen on many levels. In this chapter, the science has been presented in a basic way – for a greater understanding you may wish to find out more about some of the topics such as:

- Sound and waves
- Binary numbers and digital sound
- AC and DC electricity
- Basic electronics.

▶ TEST YOURSELF

01 What are the units used to measure volume of sound?

02 Which units are used to measure frequency?

03 What is the difference between a loudspeaker and a powered monitor?

04 Which units are used to measure the power of an amplifier?

05 How many channels of sound can a stereo amplifier process?

06 Digital sound sampling analyses a waveform a certain number of times per second – what is this number called?

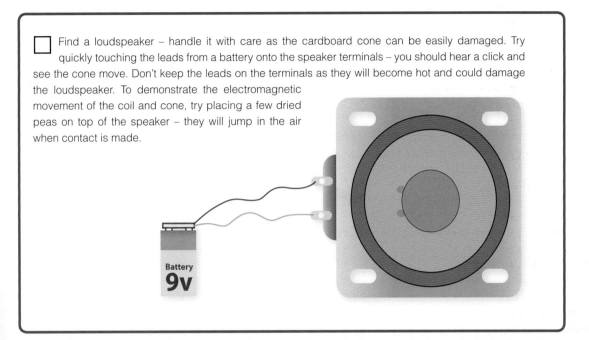

Find a loudspeaker – handle it with care as the cardboard cone can be easily damaged. Try quickly touching the leads from a battery onto the speaker terminals – you should hear a click and see the cone move. Don't keep the leads on the terminals as they will become hot and could damage the loudspeaker. To demonstrate the electromagnetic movement of the coil and cone, try placing a few dried peas on top of the speaker – they will jump in the air when contact is made.

Battery **9v**

If you can find an old or broken loudspeaker, you may be able to take it apart and look at the components inside. Seen in cross-section, it will look something like this:

Caution: The metal parts of a loudspeaker can be sharp, and cutting tools may be needed. Take appropriate precautions such as wearing gloves and safety glasses.

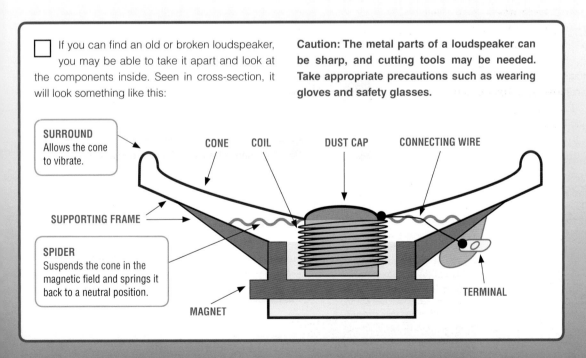

SURROUND
Allows the cone to vibrate.

CONE   COIL   DUST CAP   CONNECTING WIRE

SUPPORTING FRAME

SPIDER
Suspends the cone in the magnetic field and springs it back to a neutral position.

MAGNET

TERMINAL

CHAPTER 2
GETTING CONNECTED

CABLES AND CONNECTORS

If you play the guitar you will be used to plugging it into an amplifier. If you use a microphone with your amplifier as well, you may have noticed it uses a different kind of plug. Take a look at any mixer, effects unit or even a TV and you will see a variety of sockets and cables.

Having equipment that you want to use and not being able to join it together can be very frustrating. This chapter will explain the different kinds of cables and connectors and how they enable your audio equipment to function.

Cables are bundles of wires wrapped in an outer sheath of plastic or cloth. If they are trodden on, twisted too much or treated roughly, the internal wires can break and this may not be visible. Try to avoid taking plugs in and out of sockets by pulling on the cable as this can break the connection inside the plug.

A **connector** is a plug or jack that is soldered or screwed to a cable. They are used to connect two pieces of equipment. Wires inside equipment are usually soldered in place. Cables that run between units either have bare ends that twist around a terminal, or most commonly, connect together with plugs and sockets.

▶ TAKING CARE

Faulty cables can cause problems such as loss of sound, cracking noises and distortion. They may even damage your equipment so it is important to look after them carefully.

To check for a faulty cable, use a cable tester. This checks whether each wire has continuity – i.e. whether or not an electrical current can flow through it uninterrupted from one end to another.

▶ AC AND DC

Cables carry electricity creating an electrical current which flows in a circuit. There are two types of electrical current you will come across:

● **Direct Current (DC):** electricity flows from one side of the battery to the other (for example in a simple battery-and-light-bulb circuit). It is often described as going from positive to negative.

● **Alternating Current (AC):** the electricity rapidly changes direction from positive to negative. This is the kind of current that creates an audio signal.

> **FACT**
> If you tried the suggestion in Chapter 1 of touching the battery wires to loudspeakers, you will have heard a single click as you touched the wire to the speaker. This is because the coil was pulled one way by the magnet and then stopped. If the electricity was alternating then the loudspeaker cone would be pulled rapidly back and forth, and would generate a continuous sound.

▶TS JACK PLUG

One of the most common types of connector you will use is a TS (tip-sleeve) jack plug. It has two wires inside, which attach to the sleeve and the tip of the connector. When it is pushed into a socket, the sleeve and tip touch two different metal contacts. From these contacts, wires connect to the circuitry of the equipment.

TS JACK PLUG

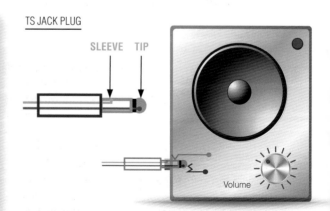

SLEEVE   TIP

Volume

BALANCED AND UNBALANCED

▶ UNBALANCED CABLES

An unbalanced cable has just two wires. Both wires carry the audio signal, and sometimes one of them is also connected to **earth**. In practice, this means that one wire also connects to the casing of the equipment so that the various units being used are linked. Most equipment with a metal casing (or frame) will also have the case connected to the earth wire of the mains supply. Properly-earthed audio circuits are less likely to suffer from interference and hum. In a well-designed studio, the electrical supply will be separate from other circuits in the building and will have a special earth connection.

FACT
In the early days of electricity, one side of a radio or tele-phone circuit was actually connected to a metal rod buried in the earth.

Earth connection

Amplifier circuit

Volume

EARTH CONNECTION

▶ BALANCED CABLES

Some cables have a separate earth wire together with two signal wires. These are called balanced cables. The two signal wires are often twisted around each other, and this helps them to cancel out any interference or electromagnetic effects which are caused by the flow of electricity.

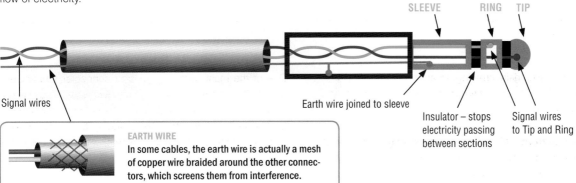

SLEEVE   RING   TIP

Signal wires

Earth wire joined to sleeve

Insulator – stops electricity passing between sections

Signal wires to Tip and Ring

EARTH WIRE
In some cables, the earth wire is actually a mesh of copper wire braided around the other connec-tors, which screens them from interference.

▶ STEREO TRS JACK

Balanced cables often use a TRS jack connector and socket to connect to audio equipment. TRS stands for tip-ring-sleeve – the three parts of the connector that conduct the electrical signal. The earth wire is connected to the sleeve and sometimes also to the casing of the connector. The tip and the ring carry the two signal wires.

If you look at the connector on the headphone lead of your personal stereo, you will see that it is a miniature TRS connector. In this case, the left stereo signal comes from the tip and the right signal from the ring. The sleeve is connected to the earth wire, which completes the circuit of both signal wires. The use of a TRS jack in this way means that it is sometimes known as a stereo jack, which is balanced. An unbalanced, two-wire jack is known as a mono jack.

TIP
It's important to find out whether the equipment you buy can use balanced or unbalanced cables – some-times using the wrong type of cable can cause damage.

21

It's worth investing in the best-quality cables you can afford. Cheap, poor-quality cables can introduce noise into your recordings and performances, and may fail at a crucial moment!

▶ KEEPING BALANCED

If your equipment is able to use balanced cables, then try to use them whenever possible. They will give the best signal, and will help to prevent interference, noise and hum (often caused by mains power cables).

▶ COMBINATIONS

A cable can have any combination of connectors at its two ends.

Common types of cable include:

- **Jack** to **jack**

- **Stereo jack** to **stereo jack**

- **Stereo jack** to **two mono jacks** (Y lead)

- **Stereo jack** to **two phono jacks** (Y lead)

- **XLR** (male) to **XLR** (female)

- **XLR** (female) to **jack** or **stereo jack**

- **XLR** (male) to **jack** or **stereo jack**

- **Phono** to **phono**

- **Phono** to **jack**

- **DIN** to **DIN** (MIDI cable).

▶ XLR MALE

These very strong connectors have become the standard for most microphone and other high-quality connections.

They have three pins, which are numbered on the plug. The earth wire is sometimes braided as a shield around the signal wires.

XLR cables can be wired as balanced or unbalanced connections.

▶ RCA / PHONO

RCA connectors are named after a famous audio company (the Radio Corporation of America). They are also known as **phono** connectors.

They have two unbalanced wires and are often twinned for use as left and right. Right is usually coloured red and left can be any other colour – most often grey or white.

You may well have seen these connectors on your home stereo equipment or TV.

▶ XLR FEMALE

A standard microphone cable has a male XLR at one end and a female XLR at the other, which slots onto the pins of the microphone.

The cable length can be increased by joining two or more together, male to female.

▶ DIN (MIDI CABLE)

DIN connectors can have a wide range of different pin patterns within a standard type of plug housing.

The most commonly used today are for MIDI connections, and have a semicircle of pins (usually five).

Although they may look the same, not all DIN cables are wired in the same way and it is important to use specific MIDI cables to prevent damage to your keyboards or modules.

▶ MONO TS JACK PLUG

This is one of the simplest connectors. The mono jack has two internal wires, one of which is usually earthed to the casing of the connector.

Mono jacks are commonly used to send single mono signals, for example from a guitar or a keyboard.

▶ ADAPTERS

If you don't have a suitable cable, an adapter (or converter) may help.

For example, jack plugs can be converted to phono or from large to small. Almost any combination is available.

Adapters can be problematic, though – sometimes loose, or awkward in size or placement – so they should only be used as a temporary solution.

▶ STEREO TRS JACK PLUG

In the picture *above* the tip, ring and sleeve can be seen clearly, as described on page 21.

The three connections make this a versatile connector which can be used for a balanced signal, a stereo connection or with a Y lead for taking a signal both out and back into the same socket (see Inserts in **Chapter 5**).

Stereo jack plugs are used to transmit stereo signals, for example the headphones for your MP3 player.

▶ Y LEAD

The most common use of a Y lead is to separate the two signal wires coming from a TRS jack, and send them to two other mono connectors.

The other end of the lead could have two mono jacks or two phono connectors. These are sometimes colour coded – red for right and grey or white for left.

All kinds of audio equipment – guitars, CD players, amplifiers, processors, mixers and many more – have inputs, outputs or both. For example, a home stereo system will have left and right outputs for loudspeakers and a series of inputs on the back panel. These will probably be labelled something like: CD | Tape | Aux | Tuner. You can see this illustrated in the diagram *right*.

Why do we have different inputs, and does it matter if equipment is plugged into the wrong socket?

The input sockets are labelled differently because of the electronic circuits that they connect to. Each piece of equipment will send out a signal at a different level and with different characteristics. Some will need more preamplification than others. Plugging in a signal that is at too high a level will result in distortion and possibly damage. Making sure that an output is connected to a suitable input is known as **matching** and an unsuitable connection is a **mismatch**.

▶ IMPEDANCE

Matching and mismatching also refer to **impedance**. This is similar to electrical resistance but only applies to alternating electrical current (AC) such as in a rapidly changing audio signal. The symbol for impedance is the letter Z.

Impedance measures the way in which an entire circuit resists the flow of an audio signal. A circuit can have a high or low impedance. Microphones and loudspeakers also have an impedance rating and it is important to match them with suitable inputs and outputs.

The TV, radio, CD player or hi-fi amplifier you use at home will be specified as 'consumer' equipment and operates with different specifications to 'professional' equipment such as the mixing desk or amplifier you will use in a studio (see page 26).

BACK PANEL OF A CONSUMER STEREO SYSTEM AMPLIFIER

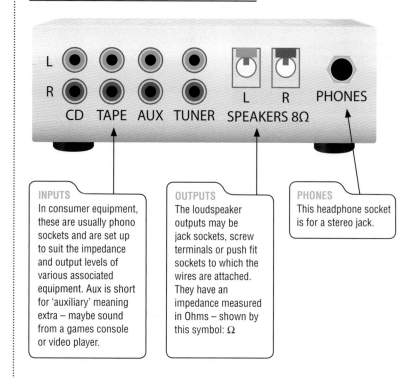

INPUTS
In consumer equipment, these are usually phono sockets and are set up to suit the impedance and output levels of various associated equipment. Aux is short for 'auxiliary' meaning extra – maybe sound from a games console or video player.

OUTPUTS
The loudspeaker outputs may be jack sockets, screw terminals or push fit sockets to which the wires are attached. They have an impedance measured in Ohms – shown by this symbol: Ω

PHONES
This headphone socket is for a stereo jack.

▶ COMBO INPUTS

For rehearsals or gigs, you may have a 'combo' guitar amplifier. This is an amplifier that includes the loudspeaker in the same casing. These illustrate well the difference between inputs: poor performance and electrical hum will be the result of plugging into a mismatched socket. The illustration *below* shows an input panel you might find on a combo guitar amplifier:

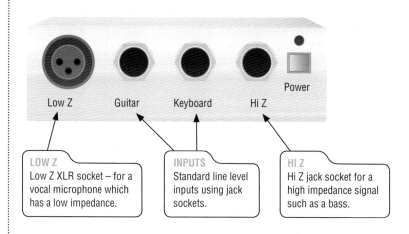

LOW Z
Low Z XLR socket – for a vocal microphone which has a low impedance.

INPUTS
Standard line level inputs using jack sockets.

HI Z
Hi Z jack socket for a high impedance signal such as a bass.

INPUT LEVELS

The most common types of input are **mic** and **line**.

If you are using a mixer you may well have these two different inputs at the top of each channel (see **Chapter 5**). They are also found on monitors, PA systems and many amplifiers. The mic input is designed to accept the very low voltage from a microphone. However, any cable coming from a keyboard, guitar, sound module or other equipment will carry a much higher voltage and should be plugged into the line input.

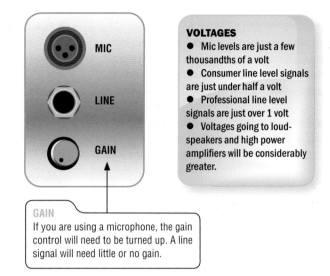

VOLTAGES
- Mic levels are just a few thousandths of a volt
- Consumer line level signals are just under half a volt
- Professional line level signals are just over 1 volt
- Voltages going to loud-speakers and high power amplifiers will be considerably greater.

GAIN
If you are using a microphone, the gain control will need to be turned up. A line signal will need little or no gain.

▶ GAIN AND VOLUME IN THEORY

In electronics, **gain** is a measure of how much bigger the output of an amplifier (or preamp) is compared with its input. This can either be just a number (for example, a gain of 10) or a figure in decibels (e.g. +3 dB). If a signal is reduced in strength (**attenuated**), then a negative figure is shown (e.g. –3 dB). A gain control is usually at the beginning of a circuit, and adjusts the performance of the amplifier.

Volume is a secondary control which affects the output signal. For every step around the gain control, there is a full range of volume that can be used.

Below is a gain and volume schematic diagram. You will see diagrams like this in the manuals of mixers and other equipment. Amplifiers are represented as triangles, and level controls as circles divided by an arrow.

GAIN AND VOLUME SCHEMATIC DIAGRAM

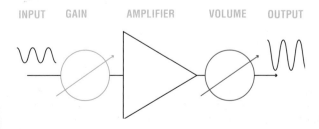

▶ GAIN AND VOLUME IN PRACTICE

To set up a microphone using the monitor shown below, you would need to turn the volume to a mid-point on the scale and then turn up the input gain until a suitable level of sound is heard.

This allows for some 'headroom' – you will be able to turn the monitor up or down in volume from midway. If the input gain is too low, the volume will have to be much higher all the time and there will be no flexibility to adjust it upwards.

▶ EQUIPMENT LEVELS

Music technology is all about electrical signal flow. Sound is turned into an electrical signal which is amplified, attenuated (reduced) or processed.

Between the various pieces of equipment, the signal travels along wires inside larger cables. At the ends of the cables, plugs and sockets join everything together.

Using the correct cables and connectors is important. Connections should be clean and firm. Loose connections will ruin your recordings with noise and lost signals.

When you are using your audio equipment, look out for level switches. On a mixer or amplifier, you may see a switch like this next to an input socket:

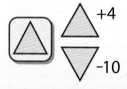

With the switch up, the input socket is set to receive higher-level signals from professional equipment.

With the switch down, it is ready to receive consumer level signals at a lower level.

The voltage levels are usually translated into decibel figures on equipment labels:
+ 4 dB for professional
– 10 dB for consumer.

▶ TEST YOURSELF

01 What does TRS stand for?

02 Which socket would a microphone plug into?
Hi Z   Low Z

03 What unit is used to measure impedance?

04 Which signal operates at a higher voltage?

Microphone   Line

05 How many pins does an XLR plug have?

06 What type of cable has two signal wires and an additional earth wire – balanced or unbalanced?

MAKE YOURSELF A STEREO CONNECTOR BOX

Amplifiers and mixers vary in the type of sockets they use for inputs and outputs. Sometimes you may want to change from one connector type to another. For example, you may have separate left and right cables coming from an amplifier for performer foldback in a studio but your headphones use a stereo (TRS) jack plug. It's easy to make up a small connector box that will make this possible.

Any kinds of sockets can be used. You may wish to add a smaller stereo jack socket for different headphones or to act as an input from a personal stereo. Any socket can be an input or output – a box like this can solve all kinds of problems. You will need to solder wires between the contacts. This isn't difficult and having some hands-on experience really helps your understanding of music technology. If you learn to solder connections you will be able to do simple repairs, saving a lot of time and money. Metal boxes for housing electronics are available, as are all the possible sockets both online and in specialist shops.

Caution: Do not use a connecting box like this to carry phantom power!

> **TRS WIRING**
> In this box, the connections are based on left and right channels. In a TRS socket, the ring carries the right signal and the tip carries the left signal.

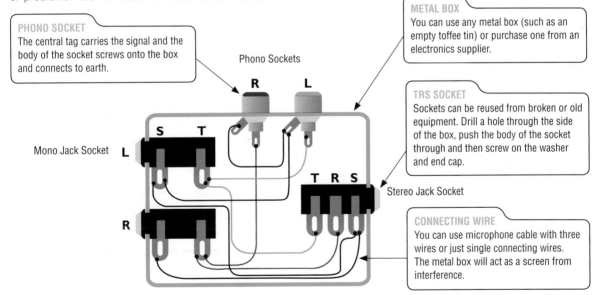

METAL BOX
You can use any metal box (such as an empty toffee tin) or purchase one from an electronics supplier.

PHONO SOCKET
The central tag carries the signal and the body of the socket screws onto the box and connects to earth.

Phono Sockets

R   L

TRS SOCKET
Sockets can be reused from broken or old equipment. Drill a hole through the side of the box, push the body of the socket through and then screw on the washer and end cap.

S   T

Mono Jack Socket   L

T R S

Stereo Jack Socket

R

CONNECTING WIRE
You can use microphone cable with three wires or just single connecting wires. The metal box will act as a screen from interference.

Find and identify some different connectors. Unscrew them and look at how the wires are connected.

- XLR connections are numbered.
- TRS jacks have a series of overlapping metal sleeves and contacts, separated by insulating rings.
- DIN/MIDI plugs have a series of pins pushing through a base.

LOOKING DOWN ONTO AN XLR SOCKET

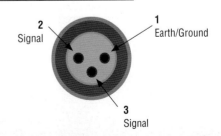

2
Signal

1
Earth/Ground

3
Signal

CHAPTER 3
MICROPHONES

MICROPHONE TYPES

▶ HOW DO YOU CHOOSE WHICH MICROPHONE TO USE?

Many factors determine your choice of microphones. Before you can decide you will need to know about:

- **The main types of microphone** (dynamic and capacitor), their characteristics and how they are used
- **Pick-up patterns:** the directions from which microphones will pick up sound
- **Frequency response:** how good a microphone is at picking up different ranges of pitches
- **Sensitivity:** how well a microphone will pick up quiet sounds.

There are large numbers of microphone manufacturers around the world and the price and quality varies greatly. It's important to understand the above factors when choosing your microphones for live sound or recording.

▶ DYNAMIC AND CAPACITOR MICROPHONES

There are two main types of microphone: dynamic and capacitor. They both work in different ways:

- A **dynamic** microphone generates its own power (like a dynamo)
- A **capacitor** microphone makes use of capacitance – the storage of an electrical charge between two conductors – and so needs to be supplied with some power. Capacitor mics are also known as condenser mics.

FACT
As the capacitor mic's diaphragm doesn't have to drive a coil, it can be much lighter and more sensitive.

▶ DYNAMIC

A dynamic microphone contains a diaphragm (a light and thin piece of material) attached to a metal coil, which is placed inside a magnet. As sound waves make the diaphragm vibrate, the coil moves rapidly in the magnetic field. This makes electricity flow in the wires, producing a very small electrical signal.

Sound wave

Diaphragm vibrates as sound waves strike it

Coil suspended in the magnetic field

Signal wires (from each end of the coil)

Magnet surrounding the coil

Audio signal leaves through the signal wires

▶ CAPACITOR

Two 'plates' – very thin sheets of conducting material – are held a tiny distance apart. A standing electrical charge rapidly builds up between them when they are positive and negative respectively. When the diaphragm plate vibrates, the charge is disturbed and electricity flows between the two.

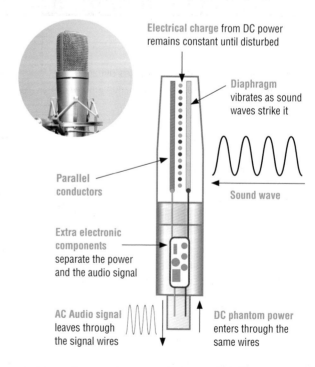

Electrical charge from DC power remains constant until disturbed

Diaphragm vibrates as sound waves strike it

Parallel conductors

Extra electronic components separate the power and the audio signal

Sound wave

AC Audio signal leaves through the signal wires

DC phantom power enters through the same wires

DIFFERENCES ▐▐

▶ DYNAMIC

1 Less expensive and more easily available.

2 Robustly made and can survive the occasional knock or drop.

3 Produces a very low level audio signal which needs lots of gain from a preamp before being useable.

4 Doesn't need a power source as it makes its own.

5 Used for close/loud sounds.

6 Less sensitive at high frequencies than a capacitor microphone. This can be an advantage in some uses.

▶ CAPACITOR

1 Generally costs more than a dynamic microphone.

2 The mechanism is delicate and needs to be handled with care. Humidity and extreme cold need to be avoided too.

3 Needs preamplifying – but not so much as a dynamic microphone.

4 Needs power – some use a battery in the casing, most need phantom power which is sent along the signal wires.

5 Can be used close up but is also good for low level and distant sounds.

6 Has a very good frequency range, sometimes up to the limit of human hearing or beyond. This makes capacitor microphones the choice for high-quality capture of complex, wide ranging sounds.

USES ▐▐

▶ DYNAMIC

1 Their strong construction makes dynamic microphones ideally suited to situations where there are high levels of sound, such as close to drums, amplifiers and loud singers.

2 Typical uses include:
- Kick drum
- Snare drum
- Toms.

3 Close mic trumpet, sax and similar instruments in loud conditions, small rooms and bands.

4 Guitar amplifier.

5 Live vocals, including hand-held microphones.

▶ CAPACITOR

1 Capacitor microphones need more careful handling and don't always survive at very high sound pressure levels.

2 Typical uses include:
- Stereo or ambient recording
- Drum overheads.

3 Instrumental recording – trumpet, sax etc. but in more controlled conditions to capture the full range of sound.

4 Acoustic/classical guitar amplification and recording.

5 Recording vocals, to capture the maximum frequency range and quality of sound.

CHAPTER 3 MICROPHONES

MICROPHONE CHARACTERISTICS

▶ DIRECTIONALITY

The shape of the microphone body and the construction of its capsule (the part that picks up the sound) affect its sensitivity to sound from the front, rear or sides. A directional microphone is designed to pick up sounds in a certain pattern. A selection of different **pick-up patterns** are shown on the page *opposite*.

▶ WHY IS THIS USEFUL?

If you are amplifiying a band or recording a number of instruments or singers, you will probably want to separate the signals as much as possible. If everyone's sound is spread across all the microphones it is difficult to adjust individual levels or panning.

If you are trying to capture the sound of one instrument and another instrument can be heard from the same microphone, this is known as **spill**. Directional microphones significantly help to reduce spill. In studios and on stage, screens are sometimes used to maintain some acoustic separation between players as well.

▶ WHAT ARE PICK-UP/POLAR PATTERNS?

These are simply diagrams which show how well microphones pick up sounds from different directions. A new microphone usually has a chart supplied with it showing how it has been tested for its response. These are sometimes called polar patterns, as they look like maps of the world seen from the poles.

To understand the pattern, imagine that you are looking down on the microphone and listening on headphones to the signal coming from it. Beneath you, someone is walking around playing an instrument. As they move into the area marked on the chart, you can hear them clearly. As they move to the edge of the pattern and beyond, the sound becomes muffled and increasingly dim.

> Pick-up actually happens in three dimensions. Sound is coming at the microphone from above and below as well to the sides. So ceiling and floor surfaces have a big effect in shaping the sound that is picked up by the microphone.

▶ WHAT IS THE PROXIMITY EFFECT?

When you sing very close to a directional microphone, the lower frequencies are enriched. This effect is used by skilful singers, presenters and announcers to colour their performances as they move closer to or further away from the microphone.

▶ PHANTOM POWER

Capacitor microphones always need power and this usually comes from a mixing desk or recording machine. The power simply flows along the cable to the microphone at the same time as the signal travels from the microphone to the mixer (along the same wires). It is usually set at 48 volts, and sometimes the switch is only labelled with the voltage.

> **TIP**
> Balanced cables should be used whenever possible, and are essential when using phantom power.
>
> It is important to put faders down and to switch off phantom power before connecting microphones.

▪ PICK-UP PATTERNS

All-round pick-up, fading with distance.

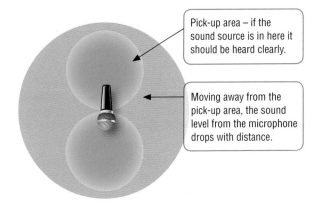

Pick-up area – if the sound source is in here it should be heard clearly.

Moving away from the pick-up area, the sound level from the microphone drops with distance.

▶ OMNIDIRECTIONAL (ALL DIRECTIONS)

Picks up sound well from all around it.

Advantages: Has a natural sound and will pick up room sounds and reflections if wanted.

Disadvantages: For individual recording there may be too much spill and room sound. Feedback is more likely in live situations.

Common uses: Ambient recording and close microphone for smaller groups or individuals where the spill can be controlled.

▶ DIRECTIONAL: FIGURE-OF-EIGHT

Picks up sound from the front and rear – but very little from the sides.

Advantages: Good for eliminating spill from the sides.

Disadvantages: Could pick up unwanted sound from behind.

Common uses: Recordings with two vocalists either side of the mic, or an interview involving two people.

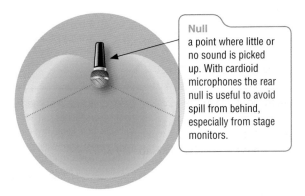

Null
a point where little or no sound is picked up. With cardioid microphones the rear null is useful to avoid spill from behind, especially from stage monitors.

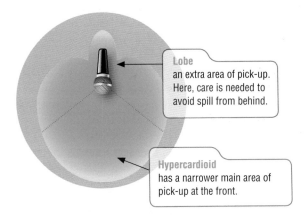

Lobe
an extra area of pick-up. Here, care is needed to avoid spill from behind.

Hypercardioid
has a narrower main area of pick-up at the front.

▶ DIRECTIONAL: CARDIOID

Picks up sound well from the front, some from the sides and much less from behind. Named from the Greek word for heart, which the shape suggests.

Advantages: Mainly focused to the front, so little spill or room noise picked up.

Disadvantages: Needs to be used with care for close microphone vocals, as a 'boxy' sound can result depending on the acoustic space.

Common uses: Close-mic recording and live sound in many situations. Cardioid mics are used to create an ambient stereo coincident pair.

▶ DIRECTIONAL: HYPERCARDIOID

Similar to cardioid but more focused to the front and has some side rejection.

Advantages: Greatly reduces the possibility of spill. Can help avoid feedback in live situations.

Disadvantages: Will pick up some sound immediately to the rear.

Common uses: Any situation in which spill is a problem, such as close-mic drums. Also useful for stage sound, where directional focus and side rejection is important.

In any microphone, a diaphragm of some kind has to vibrate to transfer the sound wave to an audio signal.

To do this easily, the diaphragm needs to be very thin and flexible. Today, these are made of specially designed materials, sometimes only a few microns (thousandths of a millimetre) thick. In capacitor microphones, the diaphragm material is coated with a good electrical conductor such as gold.

Microphones vary in size. When they were first invented they were necessarily very large. Now they can be made small enough to fit on a circuit board and be barely visible, such as in mobile phones.

Very small microphones are also available for live sound. Some miniature capacitor microphones can capture very high-quality signals.

Capacitor microphones in particular vary in the size of their diaphragms. A larger diaphragm is often used for vocal recording – these are likely to have a wide frequency range and a 'warm' sound, responding well to the singer being directly in front (on-axis).

If you hold a large capacitor microphone up to a window, you may be able to see the diaphragm silhouetted inside the casing (see *right*). Smaller microphones have the diaphragm and associated pick-up mechanism enclosed in a 'capsule'.

Capacitor microphones with a small diaphragm are more commonly used for instrumental and ambient recordings, often off-axis (not directly in front of the sound source).

▶ HIGH SOUND PRESSURE LEVELS

A kick drum microphone will have to withstand tremendous levels of air pressure when it is placed next to or inside the skin. Specialist, heavy-duty dynamic microphones are made for this purpose.

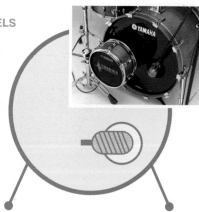

▶ POP SHIELDS

When speaking or singing some consonants such as 'p' or 'b', a powerful blast of air heads towards the microphone and can cause unwanted noise. These consonant sounds are called 'plosives'.

To prevent these sounds from being picked up by the microphone, you can use a pop shield. This consists of a thin fabric stretched across a circular frame. The fabric breaks up the pressure wave from the plosive and prevents the intrusive noise that would result. You can see an example of this *below*.

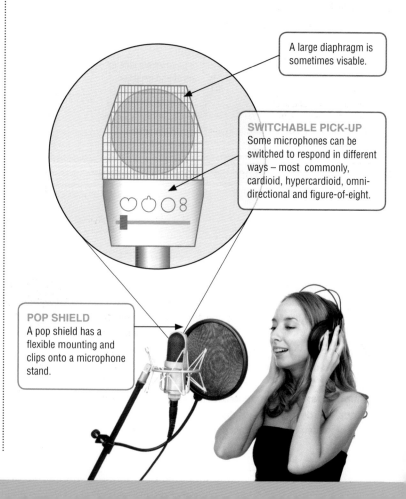

A large diaphragm is sometimes visable.

SWITCHABLE PICK-UP
Some microphones can be switched to respond in different ways – most commonly, cardioid, hypercardioid, omni-directional and figure-of-eight.

POP SHIELD
A pop shield has a flexible mounting and clips onto a microphone stand.

FREQUENCY RESPONSE

The range of frequencies that we can hear is roughly from 20 Hz to 20 kHz. We don't hear evenly across this range, and neither do microphones. Manufacturers supply charts showing which frequencies are more favoured or rejected by their products. Some are designed with particular instruments or circumstances in mind, and it is well worth having a look at the booklet that comes with your microphone.

When you sing or play an instrument, **overtones** are produced as well as the main (fundamental) note. These are additional notes at frequencies above the fundamental that add character to the sound. For example, although the fundamental notes you sing are likely to be in the range 100

Hz to 1 kHz, the overtone frequencies around 5 kHz are very important for the 'presence' of the voice. You can hear this by adjusting the EQ on a mixer while singing into a microphone that runs through it.

It's very important to capture the overtones of a sound for good-quality recording or amplification. The chart below shows how the capture response of a typical **dynamic** vocal microphone varies from low to high frequencies. Capacitor microphones generally have a wider frequency range that is captured more evenly, so the chart will be flatter across more of the range.

This chart shows the frequency response of a typical dynamic vocal microphone. The chart is not to scale, but is divided into frequency bands, each covering approximately one octave. Notice how at high and low frequencies the microphone picks up sounds less strongly.

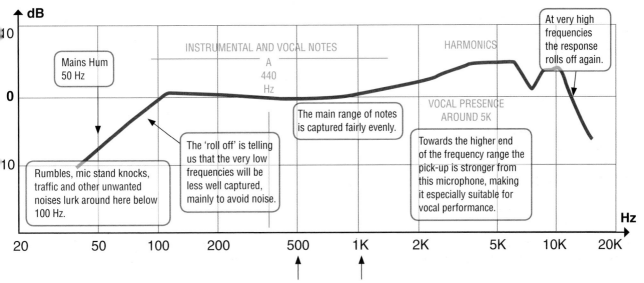

Each doubling of frequency represents a change of one octave

▶ ROLL-OFF

Some microphones have a switch that will reduce the sensitivity below a certain frequency to help reduce unwanted noise. The symbol for this looks like the sharp slope at the beginning of the frequency response graph *above*.

KICK DRUM MICROPHONE

The shape of the microphone body, the size of the diaphragm and the design of the pick-up components all affect the frequency response and general sensitivity. A set of drum microphones will include specialist microphones for kick drum, snare, high and low toms as well as overheads. They will vary in shape and size to reflect their different purposes.

▶ MICROPHONES

In recent times the quality of microphones has improved while their price has steadily reduced.

If your budget is tight, a good choice for multi-track recording is to get a set for drums plus one or two good-quality vocal or instrumental microphones.

Large-diaphragm capacitor microphones are a popular choice for vocals. They are usually supplied with a 'spider' suspension mount, which prevents them picking up noise from vibration.

It's a good idea to keep your microphones in the original cases or a foam-lined flight case. Dynamic ones tend to be more rugged but any microphone will be damaged with very rough handling.

Use the best-quality cables you can afford and avoid treading on them. Always lower the faders on your mixer and turn off the phantom power before connecting.

Modern dynamic microphones are usually designed to ignore phantom power, but it is a good idea to turn it off to avoid surges of power through mixers and loudspeakers when you connect them.

▶ TEST YOURSELF

01 What is the proximity effect?

02 Which type of microphone can use phantom power?

☐ Dynamic   ☐ Capacitor

03 Which type of microphone has a wider frequency range?

☐ Dynamic   ☐ Capacitor

04 Which polar pattern shows sound being picked up from all around the microphone?

05  Why do some microphones roll off the low frequencies?

06 What is the approximate frequency range of human hearing?

☐ **Look at as many microphones as you can**. If you're at a school or college offering music technology, there should be a range of microphones available. Compare the shapes and sizes of the various types.

☐ **Read the leaflets that come with the microphones** – most have a pick-up chart and a frequency response graph. They often have a description of the characteristics with recommended uses and positioning.

☐ **Become familiar with the well-known manufacturers and microphone types**. Some have been studio favourites for decades, and some are new to the market.

Look through magazines and websites and visit shops – you will soon notice the microphones that have made a name for themselves.

☐ **Look inside a microphone**. On some, the body or top section will unscrew. Some have adaptors to change the polar pattern. You may come across one that is broken and can be taken apart to view the structure.

☐ **Find some articles about microphone positioning**. There is an enormous amount to be learnt about using them well.

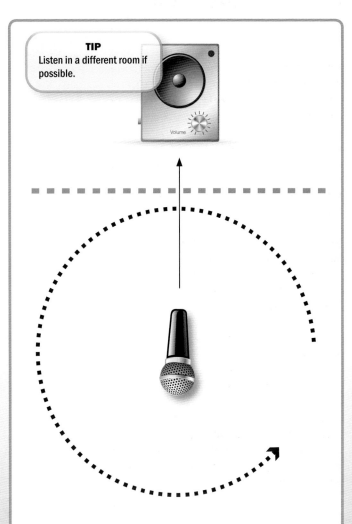

TIP
Listen in a different room if possible.

Set up a microphone in the middle of a large room. Ask someone to walk around it making a steady level of noise – perhaps describing where they are as they move around the microphone. Notice where the sound is strongest and clearest and where it becomes muffled and weak. Does it correspond with the pick-up pattern? Do the sound reflections from the wall and ceiling affect the result?

CHAPTER 4
EQUIPMENT

AUDIO EQUIPMENT

A recording studio can look very complicated, with lots of equipment and a great deal of cabling joining it all together. A mixer acts as a central hub with everything else connected to it. A common name for a mixer used to be 'mixing board', as it is essentially a flat panel covered in sockets and controls. Anything included in the mixer circuitry is described as an 'onboard' feature, and anything plugged into it is still known as 'outboard' equipment.

A piece of outboard equipment may be a free-standing box with controls and sockets on the front and rear. The box in which equipment is built is also known as the 'case' or 'housing', and the internal frame on which the circuits are mounted is the 'chassis'. Some units can be rack-mounted, and these have standard sizes for height and width. They also have fixing holes ready to take the rack-mounting bolts.

It's well worth getting to know some of this equipment individually, looking at the inputs and outputs, finding out what the various controls do and trying it out. In this chapter we will take a look at some of the equipment that you are likely to use in a recording or live setup, including:

Mixer: Combines and controls the audio signals from the other equipment. We'll look at this in detail in **Chapter 5**.
DI box: Matches the audio signal from guitars and other instruments to mixer and amplifier inputs.
Effects unit: Adds reverb or other effects to an audio signal which is then mixed back in with the original sound.
Compressor: Processes an audio signal, evening out changes in volume and reducing peaks so that they don't cause distortion.
Preamp: Brings a microphone signal up to a useable level at the highest possible quality.
EQ module: Boosts or reduces an audio signal within certain frequency bands – perhaps increasing the bass, or improving the sound of a voice or instrument.

▶ STUDIO SETUP

A mixer acts as a hub for all the equipment, taking in signals from microphones and equipment and sending them out again to be monitored or recorded.

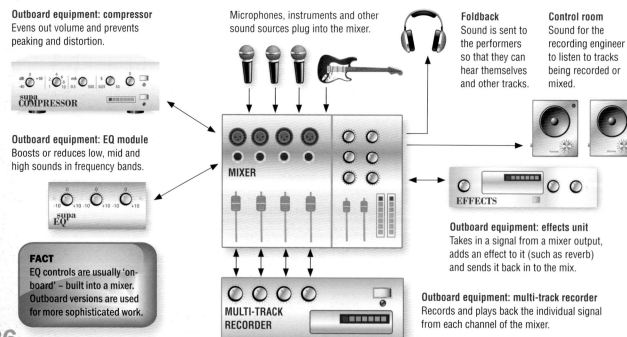

Outboard equipment: compressor
Evens out volume and prevents peaking and distortion.

supa COMPRESSOR

Outboard equipment: EQ module
Boosts or reduces low, mid and high sounds in frequency bands.

supa EQ

FACT
EQ controls are usually 'on-board' – built into a mixer. Outboard versions are used for more sophisticated work.

Microphones, instruments and other sound sources plug into the mixer.

MIXER

MULTI-TRACK RECORDER

Foldback
Sound is sent to the performers so that they can hear themselves and other tracks.

Control room
Sound for the recording engineer to listen to tracks being recorded or mixed.

EFFECTS

Outboard equipment: effects unit
Takes in a signal from a mixer output, adds an effect to it (such as reverb) and sends it back in to the mix.

Outboard equipment: multi-track recorder
Records and plays back the individual signal from each channel of the mixer.

RACKS AND PATCHBAYS

▶ CONNECTING UP

Outboard equipment can be rack mounted to help cable management and connection. A patchbay is often mounted at the top of the rack. All the other equipment is routed through this and the different units can be connected together using patch leads.

Racks can be purchased ready-made in many different shapes and sizes. Some are enclosed with a smart finish and some are fitted into flight cases for easy transport of equipment. Other accessories are available such as ventilation strips or blank panels to fill in gaps.

▶ PATCHBAY

This is a flexible way of joining equipment together. Sockets on the back connect to the equipment in the rack. Sockets on the front can then be used to join the various inputs and outputs together with patch leads. The signals pass straight through the patchbay from back to front. Patchbays can include any kind of socket.

Any signals coming in or out of a studio can be routed through a patchbay. For example, microphone cables can be wired into the back of the patchbay and then connected to mixer inputs using patch leads on the front.

PATCH LEAD

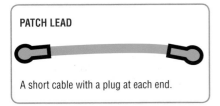

A short cable with a plug at each end.

LABELLING
It's very important to label your patchbay carefully. Outputs are normally on upper rows and Inputs on lower rows. Coloured labels can help greatly. Separate sections for mixer channels, outboard equipment and so on also help to keep things clear.

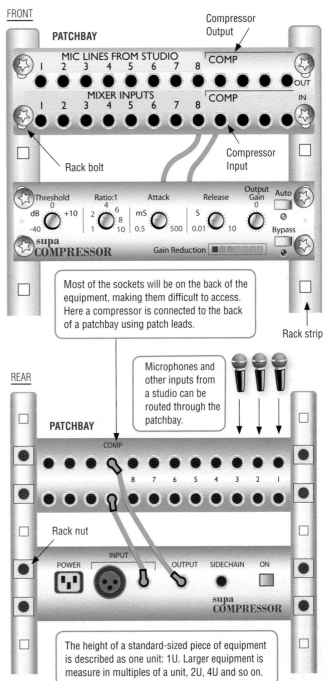

Most of the sockets will be on the back of the equipment, making them difficult to access. Here a compressor is connected to the back of a patchbay using patch leads.

Microphones and other inputs from a studio can be routed through the patchbay.

The height of a standard-sized piece of equipment is described as one unit: 1U. Larger equipment is measure in multiples of a unit, 2U, 4U and so on.

DI BOX

If you want to record or perform with an electric guitar or keyboard, you may want to plug it directly into a mixer or an amplifier. Although some equipment can accept a direct input (DI) connection from an instrument, many cannot. So, before you plug anything in, you need to make sure the signal level and impedance of your instrument are compatible with your mixer or amplifier. If not, you will need to add a DI box.

Inside a DI box, a circuit transforms the signal so that when it emerges from the XLR output socket it has a low impedance, and is at a suitable level to connect to a microphone input on a mixer or sound system. On stage it is common to plug a guitar or keyboard into a DI box, rather than directly into a sound system.

DI boxes can be active or passive. Active boxes require either power from a battery or phantom power from a mixer (see **Chapter 5**). Passive boxes simply use the incoming signal to power their circuitry.

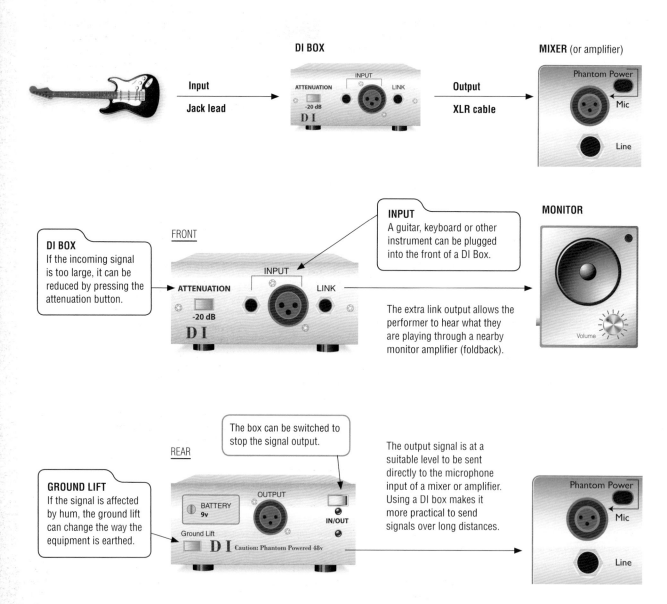

DI BOX

Input
Jack lead

MIXER (or amplifier)

Output
XLR cable

INPUT
A guitar, keyboard or other instrument can be plugged into the front of a DI Box.

MONITOR

DI BOX
If the incoming signal is too large, it can be reduced by pressing the attenuation button.

FRONT

The extra link output allows the performer to hear what they are playing through a nearby monitor amplifier (foldback).

The box can be switched to stop the signal output.

REAR

The output signal is at a suitable level to be sent directly to the microphone input of a mixer or amplifier. Using a DI box makes it more practical to send signals over long distances.

GROUND LIFT
If the signal is affected by hum, the ground lift can change the way the equipment is earthed.

EFFECTS UNIT

▶REVERB

Whether working with live music or recording, you may wish to add an effect to some of the sounds you are using. The most common effect is reverb (reverberation) which imitates the reflections of a sound that come back from the space around it. This can range from the minimal reverberation of a small room to the many seconds of echo that ring around the stone walls of a cathedral. Until the digital age, reverb was hard to create artificially and often involved sending sound through a metal plate or spring, or even playing it back in a hard-walled room (an 'echo chamber') and picking it up again with a microphone.

A reverb unit takes in a single audio signal, processes it digitally and then sends out the '**effected**' sound in stereo. A mix control combines the 'dry' original signal with the 'wet' effected signal. If the control is set to fully-dry then only the original sound will be heard.

This diagram shows an effects unit connected to a guitar amplifier. Here the guitar signal is sent to the amplifier, which then sends it to the effects unit using a 'send loop'. After the unit adds its effect, the signal returns to the amplifier.

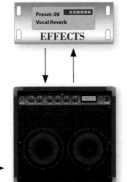

FACT
A 'dry' signal is one that has not been **effected**.

A 'wet' signal has had one or more effects applied to it.

At 100% wet, only the effected signal will be heard. With a mixer it is normal to set the effect mix to fully-wet, and then to control how much of that effected sound is mixed back in.

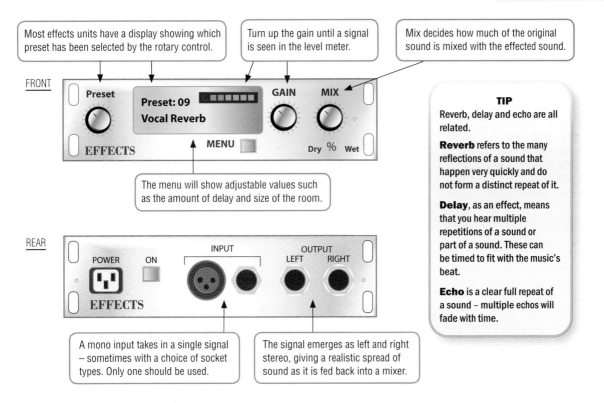

Most effects units have a display showing which preset has been selected by the rotary control.

Turn up the gain until a signal is seen in the level meter.

Mix decides how much of the original sound is mixed with the effected sound.

FRONT

Preset

Preset: 09
Vocal Reverb

GAIN   MIX

EFFECTS   MENU   Dry % Wet

The menu will show adjustable values such as the amount of delay and size of the room.

TIP
Reverb, delay and echo are all related.

Reverb refers to the many reflections of a sound that happen very quickly and do not form a distinct repeat of it.

Delay, as an effect, means that you hear multiple repetitions of a sound or part of a sound. These can be timed to fit with the music's beat.

Echo is a clear full repeat of a sound – multiple echos will fade with time.

REAR

POWER   ON   INPUT   OUTPUT
LEFT   RIGHT

EFFECTS

A mono input takes in a single signal – sometimes with a choice of socket types. Only one should be used.

The signal emerges as left and right stereo, giving a realistic spread of sound as it is fed back into a mixer.

The signals from a microphone are too small for an effects unit to use directly. They need a line-level signal from a preamplifier or mixer. However, some electric guitars and keyboards can be connected to the input of an effects unit, and this can be a useful way to experiment with effects. If you are a guitarist, you may be familiar with effects pedals, which are often very sophisticated and sometimes double up as DI boxes. We'll be looking in more detail about sending and returning signals in **Chapter 5**.

COMPRESSION

▶ DYNAMICS

Dynamics refer to the changing levels of sound when we play or sing. A compressor is a dynamics processor – it controls the level of the signal passing through it.

▶ WHY CONTROL DYNAMIC LEVELS?

When you are singing into a microphone, the dynamic range can change rapidly. Most singers move closer to and further away from a microphone as they perform. This can lead to uncontrolled levels of sound and sometimes distortion. To help with this, a compressor reduces the signal level of loud sounds. It can even out the sound of instruments too, for example making a bass guitar or kick drum sound more punchy during mixing. Compression can be used both for recording and during live events.

To use a compressor effectively, you need to set a **threshold**.

GRAPH OF SIGNAL COMPRESSION

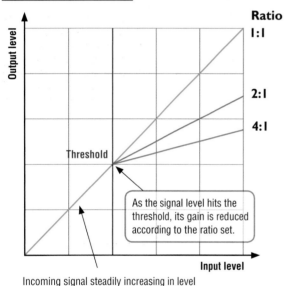

As the signal level hits the threshold, its gain is reduced according to the ratio set.

Incoming signal steadily increasing in level

1:1 With no compression, the level of the signal is unaffected as it passes through the threshold.

2:1 Any signal level over the threshold is reduced – for every 2 dB gain, only 1 dB gain is allowed.

Signal below the threshold is unaffected   Louder signal is reduced

4:1 Any signal level over the threshold is reduced – for every 4 dB gain, only 1 dB gain is allowed.

HOW THE SIGNAL IS AFFECTED BY COMPRESSION OVER TIME

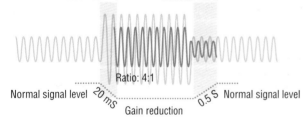

Attack: 20 mS   Release: 0.5 S

Ratio: 4:1

Normal signal level   20 mS   0.5 S   Normal signal level

Gain reduction

A compressor needs to detect an increase in level before it can react and start pulling it down. The time it takes to do this is called the **attack** time and can be set manually.

Once the signal level has dropped below the threshold again, the **release** time determines how quickly the compressor stops reducing the gain.

In the example *above*, 20 thousandths of a second after the threshold is passed the compressor reduces the gain. For every 4 dB gain over the threshold at the input, only 1 dB of gain will be allowed through. When the incoming level drops below the threshold, half a second later the compressor will allow the full level of signal through again.

COMPRESSOR

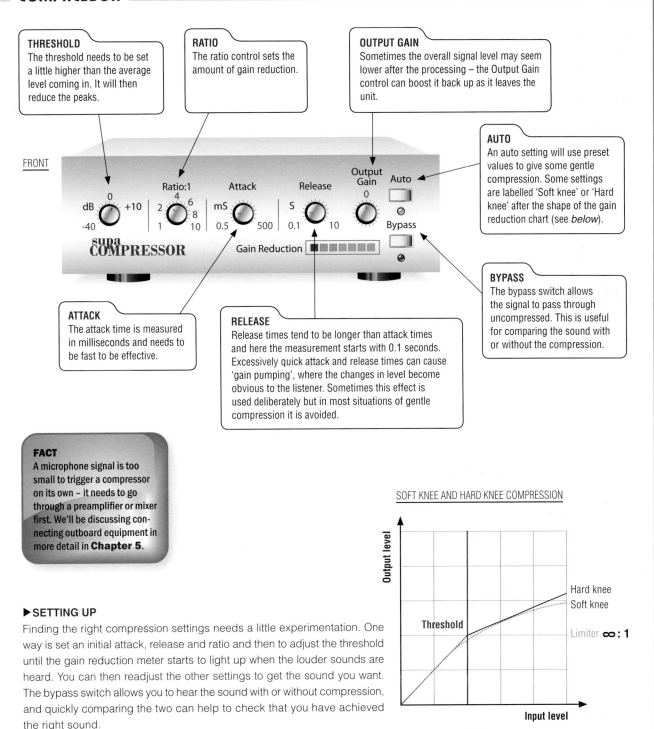

THRESHOLD
The threshold needs to be set a little higher than the average level coming in. It will then reduce the peaks.

RATIO
The ratio control sets the amount of gain reduction.

OUTPUT GAIN
Sometimes the overall signal level may seem lower after the processing – the Output Gain control can boost it back up as it leaves the unit.

AUTO
An auto setting will use preset values to give some gentle compression. Some settings are labelled 'Soft knee' or 'Hard knee' after the shape of the gain reduction chart (see *below*).

FRONT

dB 0 +10 −40 Ratio:1 4 2 6 1 8 10 Attack mS 0.5 500 Release S 0.1 10 Output Gain 0 Auto Bypass

supa COMPRESSOR Gain Reduction

ATTACK
The attack time is measured in milliseconds and needs to be fast to be effective.

RELEASE
Release times tend to be longer than attack times and here the measurement starts with 0.1 seconds. Excessively quick attack and release times can cause 'gain pumping', where the changes in level become obvious to the listener. Sometimes this effect is used deliberately but in most situations of gentle compression it is avoided.

BYPASS
The bypass switch allows the signal to pass through uncompressed. This is useful for comparing the sound with or without the compression.

FACT
A microphone signal is too small to trigger a compressor on its own – it needs to go through a preamplifier or mixer first. We'll be discussing connecting outboard equipment in more detail in **Chapter 5**.

SOFT KNEE AND HARD KNEE COMPRESSION

Output level

Threshold

Hard knee
Soft knee
Limiter ∞ : 1

Input level

▶SETTING UP

Finding the right compression settings needs a little experimentation. One way is set an initial attack, release and ratio and then to adjust the threshold until the gain reduction meter starts to light up when the louder sounds are heard. You can then readjust the other settings to get the sound you want. The bypass switch allows you to hear the sound with or without compression, and quickly comparing the two can help to check that you have achieved the right sound.

Many units have an auto setting – you just need to find a suitable threshold. This can be effective in many circumstances when a little help with peaks of sound is all that is needed. If the ratio of a compressor is set to infinity (as shown in the graph *right*), no increase in gain will be allowed above the threshold. It then becomes a limiter, something that also exists as a separate unit.

PREAMPLIFIER

A preamplifier is used for amplifying very small audio signals to line-level, before sending them to another unit for further treatment. As we read previously, some audio signals (for example, microphone signals) are too weak to interact with certain pieces of equipment.

Apart from being built into mixers, stereo systems and PA (public address) systems, preamps also exist as separate units. High-quality preamps are essential for ambient recording (see **Chapter 8**) and, when multi-tracking, they can make a real difference to the quality of the original sound capture.

A preamp takes in a microphone signal and sometimes also provides phantom power. From the output, a line-level signal can be fed to a mixing desk, recording machine or a more powerful amplifier. They are sometimes made as a pair within one boxed or rack-mounted unit. Tube (valve) preamplifiers are becoming increasingly popular for their perceived warmth of sound. Some preamps have additional features, such as equalisation presets to enhance the sound.

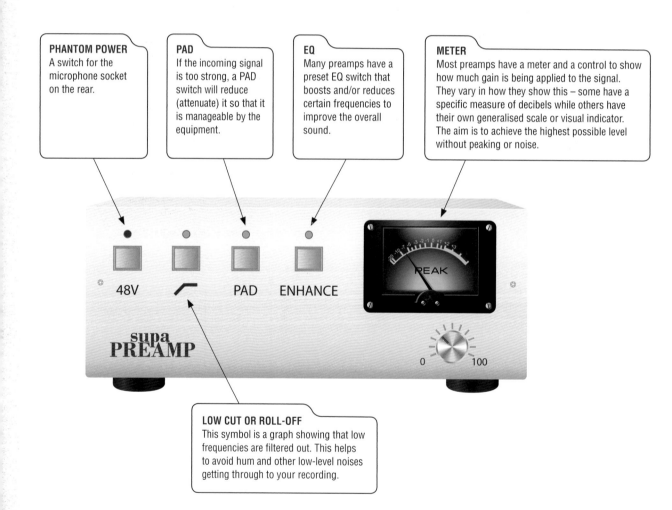

PHANTOM POWER
A switch for the microphone socket on the rear.

PAD
If the incoming signal is too strong, a PAD switch will reduce (attenuate) it so that it is manageable by the equipment.

EQ
Many preamps have a preset EQ switch that boosts and/or reduces certain frequencies to improve the overall sound.

METER
Most preamps have a meter and a control to show how much gain is being applied to the signal. They vary in how they show this – some have a specific measure of decibels while others have their own generalised scale or visual indicator. The aim is to achieve the highest possible level without peaking or noise.

LOW CUT OR ROLL-OFF
This symbol is a graph showing that low frequencies are filtered out. This helps to avoid hum and other low-level noises getting through to your recording.

EQUALISATION

EQ is short for equalisation. Using EQ can enhance a sound by increasing or reducing the frequencies that make it up.

EQ controls are common in mixer channels and on amplifiers, but can also exist as separate units. They generally have controls to reduce or boost frequencies within a range known as a 'band'. These are often labelled simply as high, mid or low, but can also be specified by frequency on more sophisticated units. The simplest EQ controls are the treble and bass features in a radio or hi-fi system. The most complex are the multi-band units used for mixing and mastering in recording studios.

With the control at 0 no equalisation is applied. Turning the control to the left reduces the level of that frequency band and turning to the right increases it.

TIP

A little EQ can help greatly when using PAs (Public Address systems):

- A slight reduction in the high frequencies can help to control the sibilance (the 's' sounds) of the spoken voice
- A little extra mid may help with the overall quality
- Reducing the low bass frequencies can prevent the voice from booming.

The voice, the venue and the PA system all contribute to the overall effect, so the best way to set up the EQ is to experiment during a sound check.

PROJECTS AND SUGGESTIONS

▶ KNOW YOUR GEAR

In **Chapter 6**, we will look at the use of computers in music technology. Almost everything you see in software studios is based on real equipment, so it really helps to be familiar with outboard hardware.

Books, magazines and websites can offer a lot of information, but you will only gain real knowledge when you combine this with hands-on experimentation.

If the only equipment available to you is fixed in a studio, ask if you can see behind the mixing desk and racks to discover how it is connected. Look at how the leads join all the equipment together and draw a flow chart of it. Perhaps you could also take a unit or two out of the rack to follow this up? If you are following a music technology course, then this kind of discovery-learning will be part of it.

Better still, get hold of some hardware on its own, either stand-alone or designed for a rack, and see what you can do with it. Audio equipment has never been cheaper or more readily available – if you are at school, your music department should have some you can experiment with.

Examine the front and rear to discover what inputs and outputs are available. What do all the controls do? If there are any you don't understand, look in the manual (often available online), refer to the relevant section in this book, or ask your teacher.

▶ TEST YOURSELF

01
DI box
Which problem may be helped by a **ground lift** switch?

02
Effects unit
What is the difference between a 'wet' and a 'dry' signal?

03
Compressor
What is the Bypass feature used for?

04
Preamplifier
The pad switch reduces incoming levels – which other word means to reduce a signal?

05
What does this symbol represent?

06
Compressor
What effect would a ratio of 6:1 have on an incoming signal that is above the threshold?

► **TRY THIS**

Find a DI box and check whether it is active or passive. If it is active, make sure it can take a battery and fit one if necessary. Look for the features described in this chapter.

Plug an electric guitar or bass into the box – it doesn't matter whether or not you can play it.

Using an XLR lead, connect the output to an amplifier mic socket.

Set the guitar volume to almost-full and the amplifier volume to a moderate level. Turn off any attenuation (or pad) switches on the DI box and strum the guitar.

Vary the amplifier level from low to high and check the range of sound. If too much is coming from the guitar, try using the Pad switch.

If you switch the ground lift, does it make any difference?

If you can find some different DI boxes, compare the features – are the switches and sockets labelled differently? Can you hear any difference in the sound quality or levels?

Experiment with a patchbay. Connect two sockets on the back of it to the inputs of two powered monitors.

Take two jack leads from the outputs of a keyboard and plug them into the equivalent sockets on the front of the patchbay. The sound from the keyboard should now come through the monitors.

Plug the keyboard outputs into two different sockets on the back of the patchbay.

Now using two jack to jack leads (patch leads) you should be able to connect the keyboard to the monitors on the front of the patchbay. Use the diagram *below* to help you.

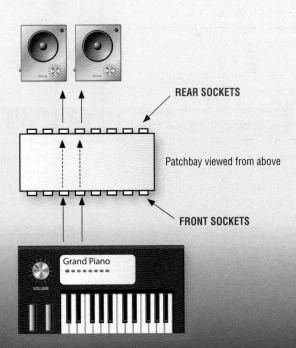

REAR SOCKETS

Patchbay viewed from above

FRONT SOCKETS

CHAPTER 5
MIXING IT UP

WHAT IS A MIXER?

A mixer provides the most effective way to connect audio signals (from microphones, guitars and so on) to other equipment such as amplifiers, effects units and recording machines.

It acts as a central point into which all your equipment can be connected. It then routes the signals coming into it to a variety of outputs, depending on its specifications.

Mixers can be found in all shapes and sizes ranging from small tabletop boxes to long consoles in commercial studios. Sometimes they are built into other equipment (such as a recorder or amplifier). They have two main uses: **managing live sound** and **recording**. Different models are designed to suit their intended use such as studio recording, theatre sound or general purpose mixing.

▶ LIVE SOUND

Mixing for a live show involves combining the sound from microphones, guitars, keyboards and other sources and delivering them to an audience through a sound system. They need to be balanced and panned and the levels may need adjusting as the show progresses.

▶ RECORDING

During studio recording, a mixer connects microphones and instruments to multi-track recording equipment and studio monitors. When all the individual tracks have been recorded, they are played back through the mixer and the final combined output is recorded separately as the master track.

A TYPICAL LAYOUT OF SOCKETS AND CONTROLS ON A SIMPLE TWO-CHANNEL MIXER

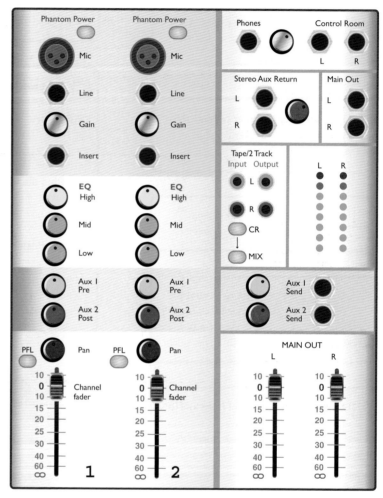

INPUT SECTION ———————▶ OUTPUT SECTION

Mixers are divided into sections, the main two being the **input** and **output** sections. The inputs are divided into numbered vertical channels. The sockets on free-standing mixers are often on the front surface as well as the back. On larger console (desk) mixers they are always on the back, keeping the control surface free of cables.

Although large mixing desks look very complicated, they simply have many more input channels, all of which are essentially the same.

MIX BUS

SIMPLIFIED VIEW OF A TWO-CHANNEL MIXER

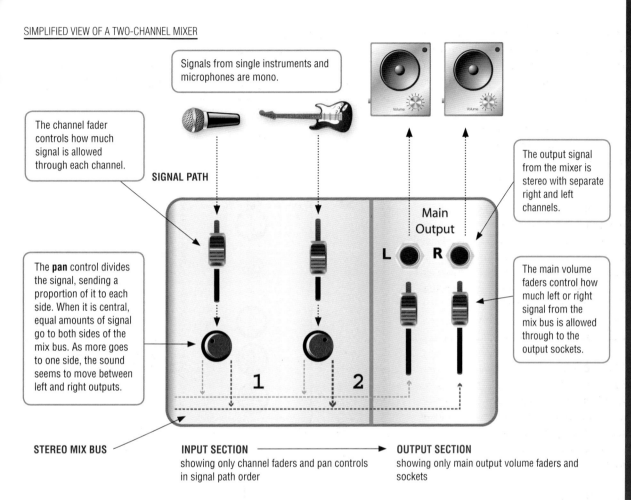

Signals from single instruments and microphones are mono.

The channel fader controls how much signal is allowed through each channel.

SIGNAL PATH

The output signal from the mixer is stereo with separate right and left channels.

Main Output

L R

The **pan** control divides the signal, sending a proportion of it to each side. When it is central, equal amounts of signal go to both sides of the mix bus. As more goes to one side, the sound seems to move between left and right outputs.

The main volume faders control how much left or right signal from the mix bus is allowed through to the output sockets.

1   2

STEREO MIX BUS

INPUT SECTION
showing only channel faders and pan controls in signal path order

OUTPUT SECTION
showing only main output volume faders and sockets

When you are working with mixers you will often encounter expressions such as **mix bus** and **effects bus**. A bus is simply a path along which an audio signal can be routed. In the early days of electricity a bus was a large wire or metal strip to which other wires were joined.

In a mixer, the mix bus is a complicated electronic circuit which can accept all the inputs and combine them before sending them to the main outputs – but the idea of wires running from left to right across the mixer is a useful way of visualising it.

On most mixers the pan control is situated above the volume fader on an input channel, but the signal actually passes through the fader first before the pan control allocates a portion of it to the left or right of the mix bus.

SIGNAL PATH
An audio signal may start in a microphone, then go into a mixer, be processed by other equipment and then finally be sent from a main mix to an amplifer and speakers.

Being able to follow a signal on its journey is an important step in understanding music technology.

INPUT SECTION

▶ MIXER STRUCTURE

The key to understanding a mixer is to break it down into sections, some of which are similar across the mixing desk.

The input section is divided into channels which are numbered from left to right. This diagram shows just one channel.

▶ HOW MANY CHANNELS?

The smallest mixer must by definition have two channels, or it wouldn't be mixing anything. Common sizes include 4, 8, 16, 24, 36, 48 and 60 channels. Some of the larger console mixers are modular – extra sections can be added as required.

▶ CHANNEL SIGNAL PATH

To understand how a signal is routed through a mixer, it is useful to think of it passing through each input channel from top to bottom.

The channel fader (which on some mixers will be a rotary control) decides how much, if any, of the signal will be allowed through to the main mix bus.

On its way through the channel, part or all of the signal may be sent out to a compressor, effects unit or for monitoring.

▶ WORKING IT OUT

If you have access to a mixer, some simple experiments will soon help you to follow a signal path through it. Using the equipment is the best way to understand it.

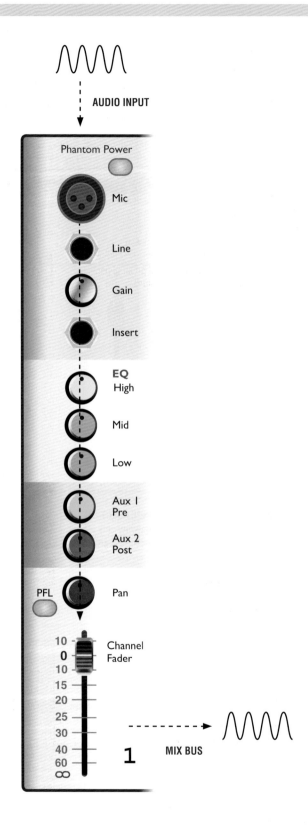

INPUT SECTION

▶ SIGNAL PATH

Here is a more detailed view of the signal path through a mixer input channel. The dotted line shows how the signal is essentially travelling from top to bottom but can be diverted on the way through.

INPUTS
Most mixer channels have an XLR socket for microphone input and a jack socket for line input. They must not be used at the same time.

GAIN
The gain control is part of the channel preamplifier, mainly needed for microphone level signals.

PRE-FADE AUXILIARY
Before (pre) it reaches the channel fader, the signal can be divided and sent to an auxiliary output.

TIP
PFL stands for pre-fade listen. When this button is pressed, the signal bypasses the fader and goes straight to the control room output.

TIP
The zero setting on a channel fader usually means that the signal is passing through that fader unaffected in level. This is referred to as **unity gain**, a starting point from which you can move the signal up or down.

On channel faders the lowest level is labelled in a different way from most other controls, using the infinity sign: ∞ or minus infinity: − ∞

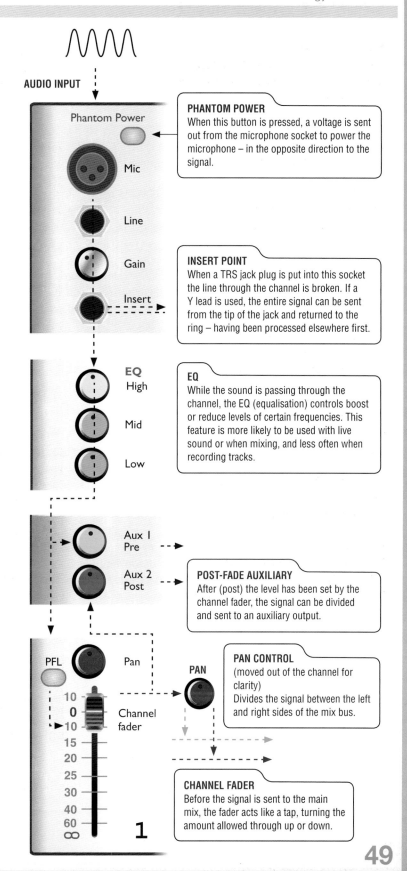

AUDIO INPUT

Phantom Power

Mic

Line

Gain

Insert

PHANTOM POWER
When this button is pressed, a voltage is sent out from the microphone socket to power the microphone – in the opposite direction to the signal.

INSERT POINT
When a TRS jack plug is put into this socket the line through the channel is broken. If a Y lead is used, the entire signal can be sent from the tip of the jack and returned to the ring – having been processed elsewhere first.

EQ High

Mid

Low

EQ
While the sound is passing through the channel, the EQ (equalisation) controls boost or reduce levels of certain frequencies. This feature is more likely to be used with live sound or when mixing, and less often when recording tracks.

Aux 1 Pre

Aux 2 Post

POST-FADE AUXILIARY
After (post) the level has been set by the channel fader, the signal can be divided and sent to an auxiliary output.

PFL

Pan

PAN

10
0
10
15
20
25
30
40
60
∞

Channel fader

1

PAN CONTROL
(moved out of the channel for clarity)
Divides the signal between the left and right sides of the mix bus.

CHANNEL FADER
Before the signal is sent to the main mix, the fader acts like a tap, turning the amount allowed through up or down.

USING A MIXER FOR LIVE SOUND

LIVE SOUND

Imagine you are in charge of the sound for a group of three performers – a vocalist with guitar and bass accompaniment. They could each have their own amplifier, but using a mixer enables you to balance and pan their sounds from one central point.

▶ GETTING READY
- Set all levels to minimum before you plug anything in. This avoids any electrical bangs and crackles as well as possible damage.
- Plug the microphone going to channel 1 into the XLR socket. This socket is sensitive to low-level signals, as discussed in previous chapters.
- Plug the guitars into the line inputs, as they have a higher signal level than microphones. If you use DI boxes for the guitars (see **Chapter 4**), plug their outputs into the XLR microphone inputs. This could help to extend the leads and to match the guitar outputs to the mixer inputs.
- Connect the main output (main mix) to the sound system for the audience. This could be an amplifier and some speakers or maybe powered monitors. The control room/headphone output lets you listen to the mix after it has been sent out, and gives you an independent volume control that does not affect the audience sound.

▶ SETTING UP
- If your mixer has a PFL (pre-fade listen) switch on each channel, you can listen to the performers without sending any signal to the audience. This switch cuts out the fader and sends the signal straight to the control room output.
- Listen to the vocalist with PFL turned on. Turn up the gain until a healthy signal is seen on the level meters. This needs to be as high as possible without going into the red (peaking).
- Set the guitars up in a similar way, using a combination of the volume on the instrument (which should be turned up quite high) and some gain if necessary.
- When you switch off the PFL, set all faders to 0 – there should be a similar level on each channel. You can then adjust the balance of the performers by listening to the sound system and moving the channel faders. One way of doing this is to leave the vocalist at a comfortable listening level and then to balance the guitars to support the voice. If someone has a guitar solo, you can 'ride' the faders, bringing the level up and down as appropriate.

▶ PAN
For a realistic listening experience, sound from the performers needs to be spread across the listening area from left to right. On this mixer, the voice is heard a little to the left and the guitar to the right, either side of the central bass. Separating sounds in this way also makes it easier to hear the balance between them. Very extreme panning can give a 'hole in the middle' effect, so it needs to be checked carefully.

▶ EQ
Sometimes the shape of a room or the nature of a person's voice or instrument will mean that the sound being heard needs some adjustment. Here we have just mellowed the sound of the voice slightly by reducing the high EQ and 'warmed up' the guitar sound a little by boosting the mid range. The bass has been left unaffected.

Now that everything is set up, you can change the whole volume of the group just from the main output faders, leaving the balance between the players unaffected.

MIXING LIVE SOUND 1

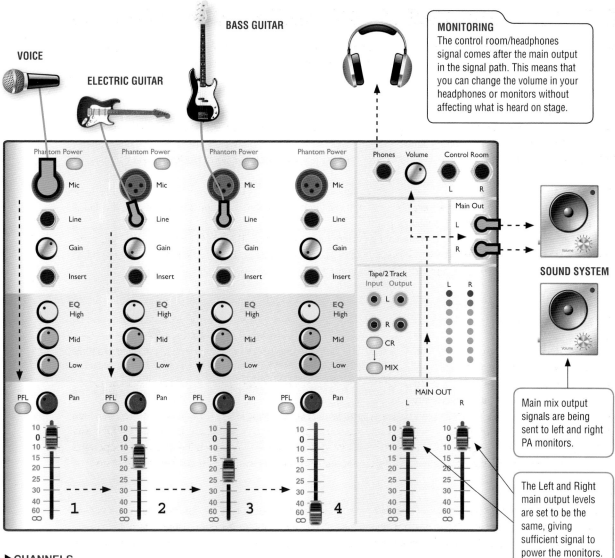

MONITORING
The control room/headphones signal comes after the main output in the signal path. This means that you can change the volume in your headphones or monitors without affecting what is heard on stage.

Main mix output signals are being sent to left and right PA monitors.

The Left and Right main output levels are set to be the same, giving sufficient signal to power the monitors.

►CHANNELS

❶ Vocal: The gain has been raised to bring the voice to a comfortable listening level. The singer is panned a little to the left and high frequencies are slightly reduced.

❷ Electric guitar: The instrument is plugged directly into the line input and only a little gain is needed (a DI box could be used). The guitar is panned slightly to the right and has a small boost to the 'mid' frequency range.

❸ Bass guitar: A strong signal is coming in here, so zero gain is used and the fader is lowered to balance the mix. The bass is panned centrally with no change to the EQ settings.

❹ Spare: This channel has not been used, so it is important to set all the controls to their minimum levels. This prevents any noise going to the main mix.

(In this illustration some of the mixer features have been left out for clarity.)

TIP
If a PFL facility is not available, set the faders to 0 and adjust the gain to give a good meter reading and comfortable sound level. This leaves some 'headroom' for the faders to move up and down as required.

▶ AUXILIARY SENDS

In our live music set-up, it could be that the guitarists are placed behind the vocalist. They may have trouble hearing the vocals or even each other. The answer to this is **foldback** – an additional output from the mixer sent to a monitor near the performer.

For foldback, use the **pre-fade auxiliary send**.

WHAT DOES AUXILIARY MEAN?

Auxiliary means 'extra' – an additional signal path. Auxiliaries are 'pre' (before) fader or 'post' (after) fader, referring to their position in the channel signal path. They are usually numbered and abbreviated to Aux 1, Aux 2 and so on, and are often colour-coded. The same colour will be seen on the controls from left to right across the mixer. On larger mixers there could be any number of auxiliary sends, some of which may be switchable between pre and post. Some mixers have auxiliary outputs specially designated for foldback.

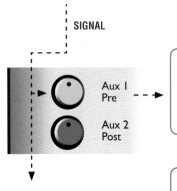

SIGNAL

Aux 1
Pre

Aux 2
Post

As the signal passes through the input channel, it is connected to the pre-fade auxiliary control before going on to the fader and pan controls. This means that the level of the auxiliary output will be unaffected by the channel fader.

A separate foldback mix can be set up which may be different to the main mix – to suit the performer's needs rather than the audience. The overall level of this can be adjusted by the Aux Send control and will not be changed if the sound is adjusted for the audience.

FOLDBACK MONITOR
These monitors are often rectangular and angled up toward performers.

THE SIGNAL PATH ACROSS THE MIXER
(only two channels are shown)

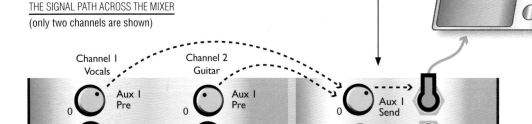

Channel 1
Vocals

Channel 2
Guitar

Aux 1 Pre · 0
Aux 2 Post · 0

Aux 1 Pre · 0
Aux 2 Post · 0

Aux 1 Send · 0
Aux 2 Send · 0

INPUT SECTION

OUTPUT SECTION

VOCAL CHANNEL 1
As the Aux 1 control is turned up, the vocal signal is sent to the Aux 1 Send control. The main signal to the fader and the mix is unaffected.

GUITAR CHANNEL 2
As the Aux 1 control is turned up, the guitar signal is sent to the Aux 1 Send control – a little bit less than the vocal in this case.

AUX SEND LEVEL
The signals from all the Aux 1 controls are 'summed' (combined) as they pass from left to right across the mixer. This is an auxiliary bus – an extra route through the mixer. The final send control decides how much of this combined signal is fed to the auxiliary send socket.

MIXING LIVE SOUND 3

SIGNAL

Aux 1
Pre

Aux 2
Post

PFL   Pan

10
0
10   Channel
15   fader
20
25
30
40
60
∞   **1**

THE SIGNAL PATH ACROSS THE MIXER
(only two channels are shown)

Using an auxiliary bus means that several
channels can use the same effects unit. The
auxiliary controls on each channel adjust how
much signal from each sound are sent to the
effects unit. In this case the vocal will have
more reverb than the guitar.

▶EFFECTS

To add some interest or to help blend the
sounds together, you may wish to add an
effect such as **reverb**.

For effects, use the **post-fade auxiliary send**.

As the signal passes through the input
channel, it goes through the channel fader.

As it leaves the fader it is connected back to
the post fade auxiliary control. This means
that only the level already let through by the
channel fader can go to the auxiliary bus.
For example, if the channel fader is right
down, nothing will be heard from the post-
fade auxiliary control on that channel.

TIP
An auxiliary signal sent to an
effects unit has to be 'returned'
so that the effect can be heard.
An auxiliary return is simply an
input socket from which the
signal is fed back to the main
mix. This is often located in the
output section of the mixer so
that sends and returns can be
located together.

The words send and return are
used to mean output and input.
If an auxiliary return is not available, the returning signal can go
to a spare channel and then be
mixed back in with the original
sound.

Phones   Control Room
L   R
Stereo Aux Return   Main Out
L   L
R   R

AUXILIARY RETURN
This is an input with two sockets
to accept the left and right
signals from an effects unit. The
auxiliary return control adjusts
how much of the signal is fed
back to the main mix.

SOUND SYSTEM

Preset:
Vocal Reverb

EFFECTS UNIT
This takes in a single
input and sends out a
stereo output.

INPUT SECTION

Vocal Channel 1   Guitar Channel 2

Aux 1   Aux 1
0 Pre   0 Pre

Aux 2   Aux 2
0 Post 0 Post

OUTPUT SECTION

Aux 1
0 Send

Aux 2
Send

AUX SEND LEVEL
The signals from all the Aux 2 controls are 'summed' (combined) as
they pass from left to right across the mixer. This is an auxiliary bus
– an extra route through the mixer. The final send control decides
how much of this combined signal is fed to the auxiliary send
socket and then to the effects unit.

As the Aux 2 control is turned up on each channel, the signal
is sent to the Aux 2 Send control. The amount of signal also
depends on the channel fader setting.

53

▶PROCESSING

When a vocalist is singing into a microphone, the levels are likely to change rapidly – one moment a breathy whisper, the next a loud chorus. Moving around can also affect the level of sound being picked up. The solution to this problem is dynamic processing using a **compressor** (see **Chapter 4**).

To connect a compressor, use an **insert point**.

> **TIP**
> In dynamic processing using an insert point, the whole signal is taken out and returned to the signal path. There is a significant difference here to adding an effect using an auxiliary send, where part of the signal is sent out and then mixed back in with the original sound.

MICROPHONE INPUT

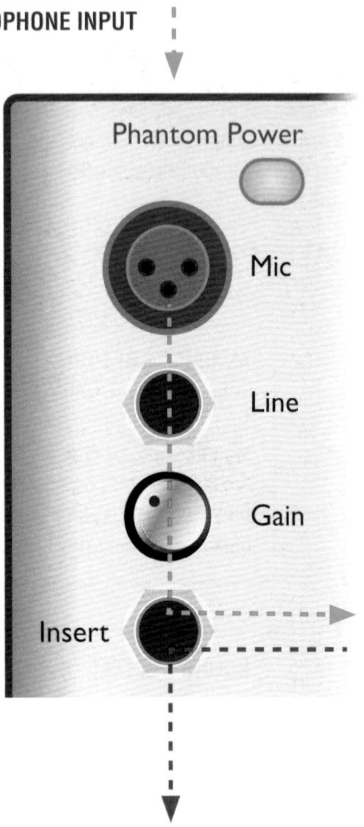

A 'Y lead' (see **Chapter 2**) is used to send and return the signal using a single TRS plug.

❶ When the plug is inserted, a spring mechanism disconnects the signal from its path through the channel and connects it to the ring of the plug.

❷ The wire from the ring goes to the tip of a TS jack plug which connects to the input of the compressor.

❸ Another TS plug connected to the output of the compressor picks up the signal through its tip and takes it along a wire to the tip of the TRS plug to rejoin the signal path through the channel.

Phantom Power

Mic

Line

Gain

Insert

TIP RING SLEEVE (TRS) JACK PLUG
The uncompressed signal is sent from the ring of the jack plug.

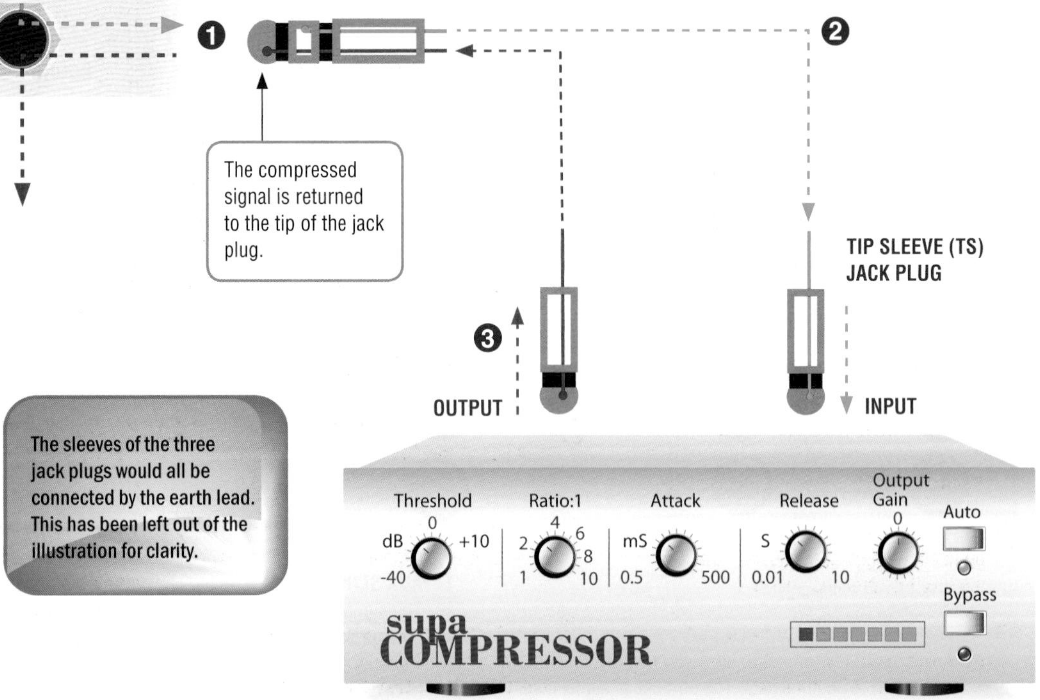

The compressed signal is returned to the tip of the jack plug.

TIP SLEEVE (TS) JACK PLUG

OUTPUT

INPUT

The sleeves of the three jack plugs would all be connected by the earth lead. This has been left out of the illustration for clarity.

Threshold
0
dB   +10
-40

Ratio:1
4
2 6
8
1   10

Attack
mS
0.5   500

Release
S
0.01   10

Output
Gain
0

Auto

Bypass

supa COMPRESSOR

MIXING LIVE SOUND 5

▶ PUTTING IT ALL TOGETHER

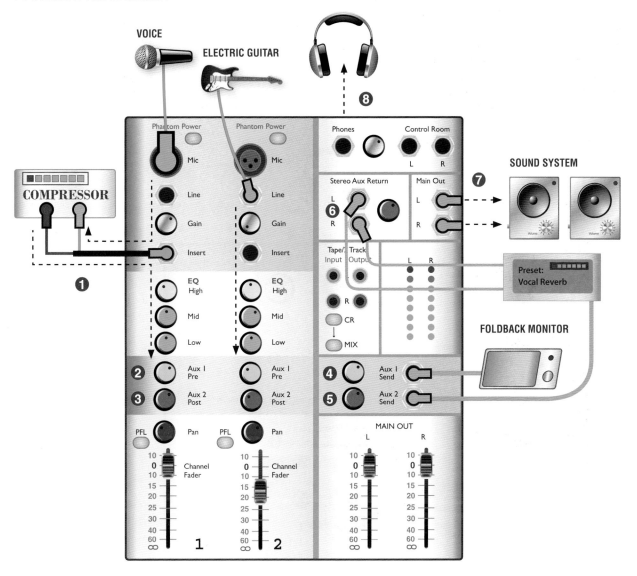

AN OVERVIEW OF THE LIVE SOUND SETUP (ONLY TWO CHANNELS ARE SHOWN)

1 The insert breaks the vocal signal path, sends it to the compressor and returns it to the channel through the same socket.

2 The pre-fade auxiliary controls are turned up to allow some of the sound through to the Aux 1 control and socket.

3 The post-fade auxiliary controls are turned up to allow some of the sound through to the Aux 2 control and socket.

4 Aux 1 sends its signal to the foldback monitor so that the performers can hear each other.

5 Aux 2 supplies the effects unit with a suitable level of signal.

6 The effected signal from the outputs of the unit is mixed back in with the main mix through the auxiliary return sockets and level control.

7 The main output from the mixer is sent to the sound system for the audience to hear.

8 After the main output, the mix continues to the control room and headphones sockets via a level control. The volume can be adjusted without affecting the main mix.

USING A MIXER FOR RECORDING

TWO-TRACK RECORDING

The main purpose of a mixer is to provide a balanced, panned mix of the sound from all of its channels, including any effects or processing. The 'final mix' has two tracks, left and right – a stereo sound – and it is from this that a master track is made (see **Chapter 9**). This could be the result of mixing a group of musicians 'live', or it could be the 'mixdown' from the playback of several tracks recorded earlier during a multi-track session.

Many mixers have a '**2 Track**' or '**Tape**' section which usually consists of two pairs of phono sockets. This offers a convenient way to record from a mixer, especially in live situations.

▶ RECORDING THE MIX

❶ The 2 Track output signal comes directly from the main mix bus. If you want to record the musicians for whom you are running the sound, for example, you can simply connect this output to the input of a recorder.

❷ The main output to the sound system continues unaffected, as does the signal to monitors or headphones, usually labelled 'control room'.

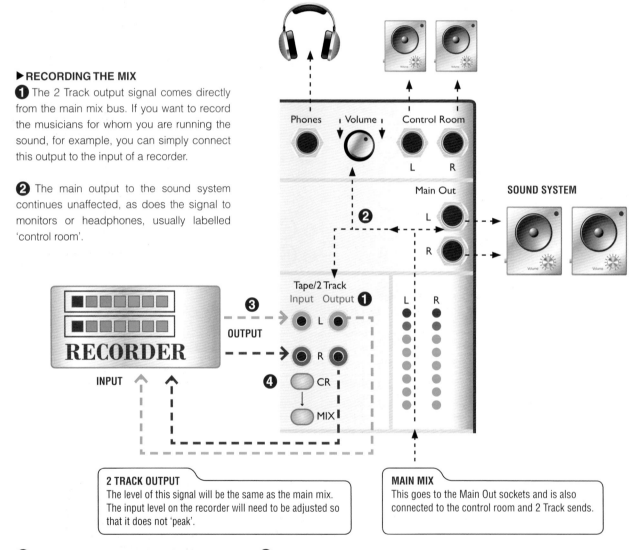

2 TRACK OUTPUT
The level of this signal will be the same as the main mix. The input level on the recorder will need to be adjusted so that it does not 'peak'.

MAIN MIX
This goes to the Main Out sockets and is also connected to the control room and 2 Track sends.

❸ If you connect the output of the recorder to the 2 Track input (return), you can monitor the sound being recorded or listen to the playback without having to plug any extra headphones or speakers into the recorder itself.

❹ As the signal from the recorder returns to the mixer, the path it follows is switchable. If you press the CR button it goes straight to the control room for monitoring. If you press the Mix button it goes to the main outputs. This can be useful for playback but would not be used during recording as it would connect the output of the mixer to its own inputs, creating a potential feedback problem.

MULTI-TRACK RECORDING

▶ DIRECT OUTPUTS

When making a multi-track recording in a studio, you will record tracks separately and mix them afterwards as a separate process (see **Chapter 8** for more on multi-track recording).

To make this possible, mixers designed for multi-track use have direct outputs and inputs for each channel, sometimes labelled as '**Tape Send**' and '**Tape Return**'.

SIGNAL PATH
The direct output/tape send socket connects to the signal leaving the channel fader before it goes to the main mix bus. Only the signal from that channel goes to the socket.

The direct input/tape return is simply an extra line-level input to the channel. Some mixers have separate faders for direct/tape returns.

Some mixers have a switch which lets you choose to hear the input from the return socket or the instrument/microphone plugged into the main channel inputs.

REAR PANEL OF MIXER

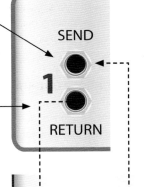

SEND

1

RETURN

Mic / Tape

10
0
10
15
20
25
30
40
60
∞

Channel Fader

1

MULTITRACK RECORDER

OUTPUT

1 2 3 4

INPUT

SEND   SEND   SEND   SEND

1   2   3   4

RETURN   RETURN   RETURN   RETURN

REAR PANEL OF MIXER

TIP
While recording the individual channels you are still able to hear a mix of them all using the main and control room outputs.

▶ STUDIO CONNECTIONS

Mixer channels are normally matched to recorder tracks by number (as shown in the illustration *above*). To connect the mixer to your recorder:

- Connect the Tape Sends on the mixer to the inputs on the multi-track recorder
- Connect the recorder outputs to the mixer's Direct/Tape Returns.

FACT
On some mixers, the direct output/send is connected at a different point in the channel – perhaps before the fader or before the EQ section. It is important to check this in the manual.

GROUP OUTPUTS

▶ MORE WAYS OUT

Larger mixers not only have more channels but more outputs too. Group outputs are like additional mix buses and it is possible to choose which channel sends its signal to which bus, using buttons close to the channel fader. Groups have their own output faders and can also have insert points and effects sends and returns. This enables a whole group of instruments to be compressed or effected.

▶ WHY USE GROUP OUTPUTS?

Some instruments may need to connect to a different sound system, or you may wish to connect a second recorder to your mixer. There are many possible uses for extra outputs. See **Chapter 9** for more on group outputs.

▶ GROUP TO MIX

One of the best examples of grouping channels is for recording the drum kit, which may have a number of microphones set up around it.

● Once the drum channels are balanced and panned, send them to a group output and then push the group to mix button, which sends that output back to rejoin the main mix.

● Now all you have to do is move the group fader and the whole drum kit will move up and down in level without having to rebalance the individual microphone sounds.

Similar benefits are available for backing vocals and other group situations.

GROUP TO MIX
When the button is pressed, the group output is also sent to the main output sockets.

FADERS
Some mixers have one fader to control a pair of group outputs, while others have separate left and right faders.

With our previous live music setup, the guitars could be grouped so that they use a different sound system or just for a convenient way of changing the accompaniment level without altering the balance.

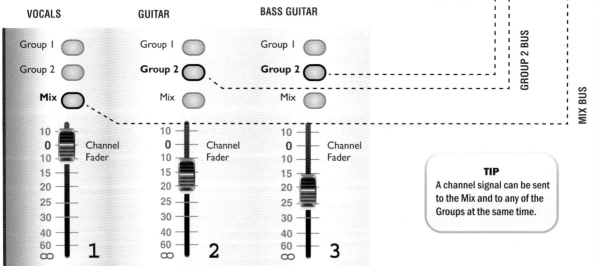

TIP
A channel signal can be sent to the Mix and to any of the Groups at the same time.

STEREO CHANNEL

▶ DOUBLE INPUT

A stereo channel has two line-level inputs and controls both signals simultaneously.

You will need to use a stereo channel if you want to plug in a keyboard, a backing track or maybe an effects return.

▶ WHY USE A BALANCE CONTROL?

If there is a difference in strength between the left and right of a stereo signal, a balance control can help even it out.

It may be that the output monitors are not evenly matched in strength or position, and this is another situation in which a balance control can help. On a mixer, the main output faders act to balance the left and right outputs of the whole mix.

A car stereo system demonstrates this well. With the driver to one side, a small adjustment of the balance control can shift the apparent centre of the stereo field, making the listening experience more comfortable.

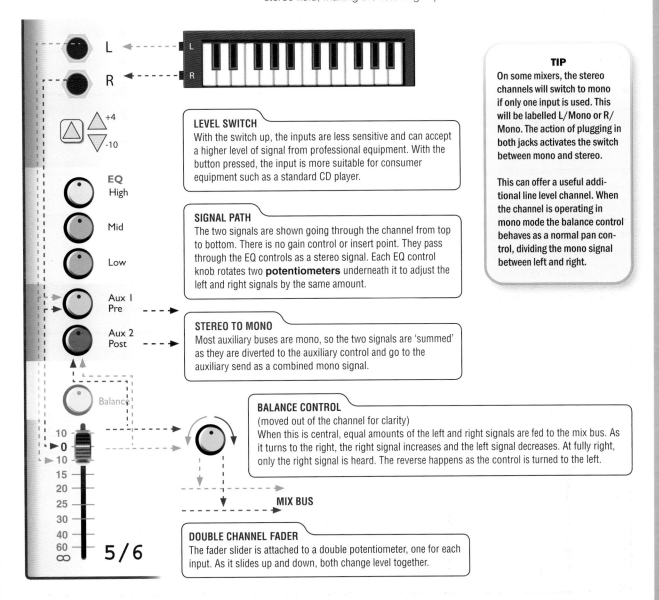

TIP

On some mixers, the stereo channels will switch to mono if only one input is used. This will be labelled L/Mono or R/Mono. The action of plugging in both jacks activates the switch between mono and stereo.

This can offer a useful additional line level channel. When the channel is operating in mono mode the balance control behaves as a normal pan control, dividing the mono signal between left and right.

LEVEL SWITCH
With the switch up, the inputs are less sensitive and can accept a higher level of signal from professional equipment. With the button pressed, the input is more suitable for consumer equipment such as a standard CD player.

SIGNAL PATH
The two signals are shown going through the channel from top to bottom. There is no gain control or insert point. They pass through the EQ controls as a stereo signal. Each EQ control knob rotates two **potentiometers** underneath it to adjust the left and right signals by the same amount.

STEREO TO MONO
Most auxiliary buses are mono, so the two signals are 'summed' as they are diverted to the auxiliary control and go to the auxiliary send as a combined mono signal.

BALANCE CONTROL
(moved out of the channel for clarity)
When this is central, equal amounts of the left and right signals are fed to the mix bus. As it turns to the right, the right signal increases and the left signal decreases. At fully right, only the right signal is heard. The reverse happens as the control is turned to the left.

MIX BUS

DOUBLE CHANNEL FADER
The fader slider is attached to a double potentiometer, one for each input. As it slides up and down, both change level together.

59

PROJECTS AND SUGGESTIONS

▶PLUG AND PLAY

Small table-top mixers are cheap and readily available. Before using a large studio mixer or working with computer based recording, you can gain valuable understanding by experimenting with one.

Most of the main functions of a mixer can be tested using the following:

- Mixer
- Headphones
- Powered monitors
- Microphone
- Media player
- Effects unit
- Compressor
- Cables and connectors.

Have a good look at your mixer and identify the features looked at in this chapter.

- How many mono and stereo channels does it have?
- Does it have pre- and post-fade auxiliary outputs?
- Does it have any group outputs?
- Is there a 2 Track section with send and return?

Every product is different, so it would be helpful if you can find a manual to go with your mixer. Manuals are often available online if you can't find a paper copy. Find some different mixers and compare their features.

> **TIP**
> Make sure all level faders are at minimum before plugging anything in and that the mixer has some space around it, as they can generate a fair amount of heat.

▶TEST YOURSELF

01 What does PFL stand for?

02 Why does a mixer have a separate output for control room monitors?

03 What is a pre-fade auxiliary likely to be used for?

04 What is a direct/tape send used for?

05 What is a 'bus'?

06 At what level would you set a channel fader to allow the signal to pass through it unchanged in level?

▶ TRY THIS

☐ **Connect two small powered monitors to the main outputs of your mixer**. Set the output faders to 0.

☐ **Plug a microphone into a mono channel (probably Channel 1).** Keep some distance between microphone and speakers to prevent feedback. Set the channel fader to 0 and speak into the microphone. Gradually increase the gain until you can hear yourself and see a signal on the meters. If you use a capacitor microphone you will need to switch on the phantom power.

☐ **If there is a PFL switch on your microphone channel, press it.** The sound should stop from the monitors. Plug some headphones in or transfer the monitors to the control room outputs and turn up the volume. You should now be able to hear yourself again. Try experimenting with the different faders to see how they all affect the signal path through the mixer.

☐ **Connect the outputs of a CD** or other player to the inputs of a stereo channel. Turn up the fader and check that the left and right channels of the music can be heard.

☐ **Make sure PFL is off**. Sing or rap along with your music track and adjust the microphone fader to balance your voice to the music.

☐ **Experiment with panning** – send your voice from left to right.

☐ **Try the EQ settings**. Turn the controls to extreme settings – squeezing out all the high or low frequencies or maybe boosting the bass.

☐ **Connect another monitor** to one of the auxiliary outputs. See if you can send the sounds from each output separately or together to it. Compare the way in which pre- and post-auxiliary work with the channel fader.

☐ **Try connecting an effects unit** to a post-fade auxiliary send, and return the effected signal to the mix.

☐ **A compressor will need a Y lead to connect it**. Plug the TRS jack into the microphone channel insert point – the sound from the monitors should stop. Connect the other jacks to the input and output of a compressor, set it to auto at first and experiment with the settings so that you can see and hear your voice levels being controlled. Press the bypass switch to hear your voice with or without compression.

CHAPTER 6
MIDI

WHAT IS MIDI?

MIDI stands for: **M**usical **I**nstrument **D**igital **I**nterface. MIDI allows electronic instruments such as keyboard controllers, computers and other electronic equipment to communicate, control and synchronise with each other.

Most commercial music of today includes some synthesised (electronically created) sounds. These sounds can be stored as samples, or can be generated by synthesisers and computer software. If you want to include synthesised sound in your production, you need a way of playing, recording and controlling it. MIDI allows you to do this.

For some years, synthesisers were too large and expensive to be widely used and performed with live on stage. In the 1970s, though, they became more compact and affordable, and several high-profile bands began to make use of them. These synthesisers were mainly keyboard-based, and some performers (notably Rick Wakeman) found themselves surrounded by keyboards, moving their attention from one to the other, even making a feature of this in their stadium shows. (Search YouTube for 'Rick Wakeman keyboard solo' to see a video of this). However, there is a limit to how many instruments one person can coordinate, and it can be frustrating if you know there are sounds available in an instrument that you can't get to.

MIDI was developed to allow electronic instruments to be linked together. For example, one keyboard could control the sounds of another keyboard. Fortunately, manufacturers realised that they needed to cooperate with each other to develop a universal control system and in 1982 the first MIDI specification was released. This listed the standard commands that manufacturers would use to make sure that their instruments were compatible.

This chapter will cover the basic MIDI messages and how they work, hardware and software sequencing.

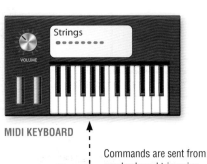

MIDI KEYBOARD

MIDI COMMANDS

Commands are sent from one keyboard triggering the other one to play notes, change volume or select sounds.

MIDI KEYBOARD

Performer – only needs to play one keyboard.

▶ **MIDI EQUIPMENT**

MIDI keyboard

A MIDI keyboard is a piano-style digital keyboard device used for sending MIDI signals to other devices. Some keyboards also include a synthesiser in their casing, and have a display for information such as which sound is being used. These can be played as a stand-alone instrument, or can control or be controlled by other MIDI devices as shown in the diagram *left*.

Master keyboard

Similarly, high-quality keyboards that only produced MIDI messages were manufactured. These are known as master or controller keyboards and have no ability to generate sound. For this reason they do not have audio outputs, MIDI IN or MIDI THRU sockets (see *opposite*), but just MIDI OUT sockets.

MIDI sound module

A MIDI sound module is an electronic musical instrument without a human-playable interface such as a keyboard. Once the idea of MIDI was established, instruments began to appear without keyboards. These included instrumental sound modules, drum machines and special-effects sounds. A studio or touring system could include a rack of different sound modules and a MIDI patchbay to distribute the data between them. This led to big changes in live and recorded performance.

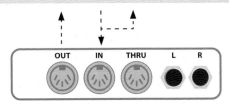

MIDI MESSAGES

▶ HOW DOES MIDI WORK?

MIDI is a digital technology and the messages it sends are strings of binary numbers.

When word processing was first invented, every letter of the alphabet was given a number. To control music in a similar way, all the notes on a keyboard were numbered, as were characteristics such as volume, pan, timbre and so on.

The microprocessors of the time used a number system with a range of 128 values. The note numbers were designed to fit within this limitation, with middle C as note 60.

▶ MIDI CONNECTIONS

Messages are sent along MIDI cables which use five-pin DIN connectors. The OUT socket sends messages. In a MIDI keyboard the IN socket receives them, sends them to the internal synthesiser and passes them out again via the THRU socket, so that additional devices can be added to the chain of connections.

MIDI NOTE NUMBERING ACROSS 88 KEYS

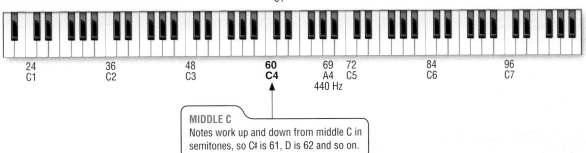

C#4
61

24	36	48	**60**	69	72	84	96
C1	C2	C3	**C4**	A4	C5	C6	C7
				440 Hz			

MIDDLE C
Notes work up and down from middle C in semitones, so C# is 61, D is 62 and so on.

▶ NOTE EVENTS

MIDI commands/messages are also called **events**.

● When a key is pressed, a Note ON event is sent to the synthesiser together with the note number.
● When the key is released a Note OFF event is sent.

With the note number, a velocity number is also sent. This measures how quickly the key was pressed and so determines the attack at the beginning of the note.

MIDI IS NOT SOUND!
It is important to remember that MIDI data is not digital audio. No sound is created until the MIDI messages are played by a software or hardware MIDI instrument.

The messages enter the IN socket of the keyboard and activate the internal synthesiser.

The sound of middle C is generated and an audio signal goes to the outputs.

MIDI EVENTS
When key pressed:
Note ON 60 100
(Play middle C)

When key released:
Note OFF 60 0
(Stop playing middle C)

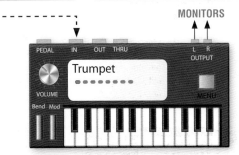

The keyboard detects Note 60 has been pressed at velocity 100 and sends messages to the OUT socket.

63

▶ **MORE THAN JUST NOTES**

Sending note events (commands or messages) to an instrument is not sufficient to make it play musically. Other information is needed about the sound (timbre), volume and any other characteristics of the note. The way this information is transmitted is detailed below.

> **TIP**
> It is also helpful to refer to the **sequence of events** table on the opposite page. It shows a typical sequence of events and the message information that is transmitted.

▶ **NUMBERING**

Each MIDI message contains several pieces of information:

1. **Event**. This tells the MIDI instrument the nature of the event: Program (selecting the sound that is used), Note ON/Note OFF, or Controller (adjusting, for example, the volume or pan of a sound).

2. **Data 1** and **Data 2**. These contain one or two parameters – numbers which set values such as volume, pan and so on. The way these work depends on the type of MIDI message:

● If the message is a **program change**, there will be just one number, Data 1, which indicates the timbre to be used (for example, 1 = Acoustic Grand Piano, 74 = Flute, and so on).

● If the message is a **note event** (either 'Note ON' or 'Note OFF'), Data 1 selects the pitch, and there will be another value, Data 2, which controls the velocity (attack) of the note.

● For a **controller message**, Data 1 will indicate the controller that is being adjusted (for example 7 = Volume, 10 = Pan, and so on). Data 2 determines the amount of effect

applied – in these examples, this will control the amount of pitch bend and the position of the pan.

All MIDI numbers are limited to a range of 128 values – these can go from 0 to 127 or (less often) from 1 to 128, depending on the device being used.

Program changes

These messages tell a synthesiser to switch to a particular sound/timbre such as a piano, trumpet or guitar. They are also known as patches, as early synthesisers changed sounds by plugging in patch leads.

A program change only has one parameter, Data 1, with the number representing an instrument. For example, a program change where Data 1 = 57 may switch the receiving instrument to play trumpet (you can see this in the table *opposite*).

Note event

A note event is the basic command to play a note, after the timbre has been selected and before the note is manipulated by a controller. The Data 1 value selects which note is being played – for example, a value of 60 will select middle C, 61 corresponds to C♯ above middle C, and so on. Data 2 indicates the velocity of the note.

Controller messages

These tell the instrument how to play the notes, for example, how loud the music should be or where the instruments should be panned. They are also known as Continuous Controllers (CC), as they can move smoothly from minimum to maximum. Some commonly used controller messages (Data 1) and how they can be manipulated (Data 2) are shown in the table below:

DATA 1 (CONTROLLER MESSAGE)	DATA 2
7 (Main volume)	Sets the volume of an instrument: 0 = no sound; 127 = maximum
10 (Pan)	Sets stereo position of an instrument: 0 = left; 64 = centre; 127 = right
1 (Modulation)	Used for vibrato: 0 = no modulation; 127 = maximum modulation. Modulation messages are sent from the modulation wheel on a keyboard
91 (Effect depth)	Adds reverb to a sound, if available in the instrument: 0 = no effect; 127 = maximum effect

MORE SOUNDS

▶ MIDI CHANNELS

Most MIDI instruments actually include a collection of synthesisers all combined into one circuit board. There are usually eight or 16 of them, and they are numbered and referred to as **MIDI channels**.

So, channel 1 may play as a piano while channel 2 could be set to trumpet, as shown *opposite*. This means that one MIDI instrument can play a complete song with many lines of music simultaneously. An instrument with many channels of sound is **multi-timbral**.

Each MIDI event begins with a channel number, so every note, controller or program change plays the correct channel.

▶ ONE AT A TIME

MIDI is a 'serial' communication system. This means that all the messages are sent one after the other. They are processed so quickly that we do not usually notice any delays, even when several notes are meant to be played together in a chord. As they arrive, the instrument sorts them out and sends them to the correct channel within a few thousandths of a second.

▶ SYNTHESISER CHANNELS

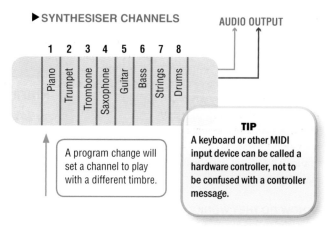

AUDIO OUTPUT

A program change will set a channel to play with a different timbre.

TIP
A keyboard or other MIDI input device can be called a hardware controller, not to be confused with a controller message.

▶ SEQUENCE OF EVENTS

MIDI messages from other devices go to the IN socket and are sent to the correct channel by their channel number. A typical sequence of events may look like this:

Channel	Event	Data 1	Data 2	Description
1	Program	1		Set sound for channel 1
2	Program	57		Set sound for channel 2
1	Controller	7	110	Set volume for channel 1
1	Controller	10	20	Set pan for channel 1
2	Controller	7	75	Set volume for channel 2
2	Controller	10	80	Set pan for channel 2
1	Note ON	60	100	Channel 1 play C velocity 100
2	Note ON	64	100	Channel 2 play E velocity 100
1	Note OFF	60	0	Channel 1 stop C velocity 0
2	Note OFF	64	0	Channel 2 stop E velocity 0

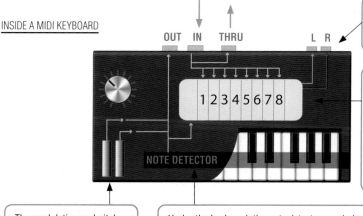

INSIDE A MIDI KEYBOARD

The synthesiser sends the audio signal from all the channels to a combined stereo output.

Synthesiser with eight channels. It can be disconnected from the keyboard using the **Local ON/OFF** setting in the menu. This enables the keyboard to operate on its own as a MIDI hardware controller without playing its own internal sounds.

The modulation and pitch bend wheels send controller messages to the synthesiser and OUT socket.

Under the keyboard, the note detector regularly checks which keys have been pressed at which velocity and sends note events to the synthesiser and the OUT socket.

The real breakthrough in MIDI-based music came with the arrival of the hardware **MIDI sequencer**, which gained popularity in the 1980s. A sequencer can record and store a series of MIDI messages and then play them back to control an instrument.

Early hardware sequencers were slightly expanded versions of MIDI keyboards. But today, they are sophisticated keyboard workstations.

▶ HOW DO THEY WORK?

● First, it is necessary to set the tempo, time signature, channel and timbre for each channel using the menu options.
● To record a song, the MIDI messages coming from the keyboard and controller wheels, drum pads or other controls are stored as you play.
● Having recorded one part, a second one can be recorded on another channel while listening to the first. In this way, eight or 16 parts can be built up to form a complete song or backing track.
● Songs can also be broken down into patterns. These are phrases that can be stored and then repeated or played in a particular order.

It is rare to find a simple stand-alone single-function hardware sequencer now. Although hardware sequencing is still a feature of many live shows, the technology is usually incorporated into a digital workstation that does a great deal more, including overcoming the limitations of eight or 16 MIDI parts.

HARDWARE SEQUENCER

A sequencer stores timing information for a song based on bars, beats and divisions of beats (such as eighth notes, sixteenth notes and so on) and will display a list of MIDI messages with their position in the song. To trigger the notes correctly it also needs to know the tempo in beats per minute (bpm) and time signature.

GENERAL MIDI

One of the advantages of MIDI sequencing is that a song can be saved as a digital file – in effect, a long list of commands. This means that a song can be transferred from one MIDI instrument to another to be played back. In the early days of MIDI, though, this was not always successful. The MIDI specification in use at that time did not specify a standard system of numbering for timbre changes, for example, which could lead to playback with a completely incorrect set of sounds.

In 1991 the **General MIDI protocol (GM)** was established. A protocol is a set of standards and GM, as it quickly became known, specified a 'sound set' of 128 timbres starting with Grand Piano as number 1. A GM instrument must also have drum kit sounds on channel 10, and all the drum sounds (bass drum, snare, hi-hat and so on) have to be associated with specifc notes on the keyboard.

Any GM file will play back correctly on any GM instrument, software or hardware. Although there may be differences in the quality of sounds, a trumpet part for example will always be played by a trumpet and volume, pan and all the other controllers will be correctly interpreted.

SOFTWARE SEQUENCING

▶MIDI COMPUTERS

As a MIDI file is a series of binary numbers making up commands, it is ideally suited for use by a computer. During the 1980s, the MIDI interface, designed to connect MIDI instruments to computers came on to the market and software sequencing applications were developed.

The Atari™ series of computers rapidly accelerated the growth of MIDI-based music, as they included built-in MIDI sockets. With a computer, a MIDI keyboard and some monitors, it was now possible to create and edit complicated sequences on-screen. This caused a revolution in music production.

▶MIDI SOFTWARE

The first software sequencing applications were pattern-based, imitating earlier hardware sequencers. It was necessary to create a series of phrases and then to set an order for playback. As computer graphics became more sophisticated and processing power increased, software was developed that showed MIDI information as tracks following a timeline. This was a big step forward, allowing the progress of every note and controller event to be seen on screen as it happened.

The computer became a hub for musical production, linked to MIDI instruments which in turn were part of a studio set-up based around a mixer. MIDI backing tracks would be produced on computer and recorded to multi-track tape, after which the live performance was added. All the recorded tracks could then be played back and mixed to make the production sound as realistic as possible.

SIMPLE MIDI STUDIO SETUP

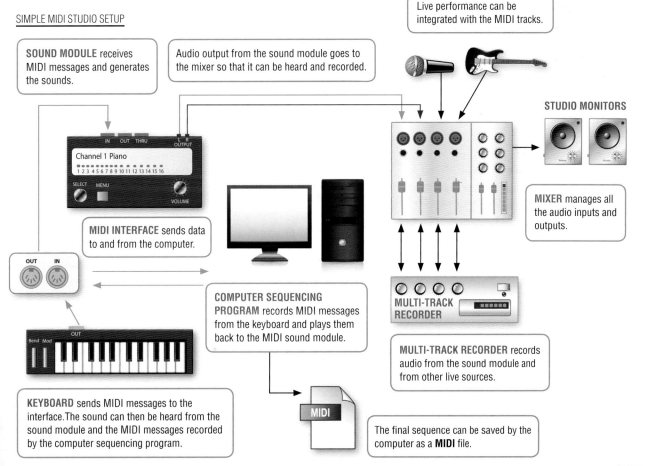

Live performance can be integrated with the MIDI tracks.

SOUND MODULE receives MIDI messages and generates the sounds.

Audio output from the sound module goes to the mixer so that it can be heard and recorded.

STUDIO MONITORS

MIDI INTERFACE sends data to and from the computer.

MIXER manages all the audio inputs and outputs.

COMPUTER SEQUENCING PROGRAM records MIDI messages from the keyboard and plays them back to the MIDI sound module.

MULTI-TRACK RECORDER records audio from the sound module and from other live sources.

KEYBOARD sends MIDI messages to the interface. The sound can then be heard from the sound module and the MIDI messages recorded by the computer sequencing program.

The final sequence can be saved by the computer as a **MIDI** file.

▶ MIDI EVERYWHERE

Keyboards, synthesisers and sound modules are still very important both for performance and recording. Because they often connect to computers with USB and other interfaces, the fact that they are controlled by MIDI is easy to overlook.

An understanding of basic MIDI hardware and commands is very useful when moving on to using software synthesisers and entirely computer-based production systems. It is also essential if you are setting up a system using both software and hardware to make music.

MIDI is not just confined to keyboards. There are MIDI drum pads, wind controllers and guitars – almost anything can be adapted to translate the actions of performers into command. MIDI can also be used for lighting, controlling explosions and special effects including computer animation.

Although most users are unaware of it, music notation software is based on MIDI sequencing. Information on the pitch, length, volume and all the other characteristics of notes is stored.

As well as being played back, MIDI information can be interpreted by the computer to create graphic shapes for the notes, rests and other symbols. Notation software does not make or record sound – it always has some connection to a MIDI instrument, software or hardware, which plays back the stored information. This could be a software program or the MIDI data can be sent out to studio equipment.

▶ TEST YOURSELF

01 What does MIDI stand for?

02 What is the most common range of numbers used by MIDI controllers?

03 What does a MIDI sequencer do?

04 How are the three common MIDI connectors labelled?

05 Why does a master keyboard usually not have a MIDI IN socket?

06 What effect does sending a program change have?

☐ **Examine all the keyboards** you can find. At school or college, you may have classrooms with keyboards connected to computers or just on their own.

● Do any of them have built-in sounds?
● Do they have drum pads or rotary controllers?
● Do they have MIDI sockets or just USB or similar computer-based connections?

☐ **Once you have found a MIDI keyboard** that has internal sounds, look at the menu and options available.

● Can you select a channel and change the sound (program), volume and pan for that channel?
● Is there a Local ON/OFF setting?

☐ **MIDI control**
Find two keyboards with MIDI sockets and internal sounds.

● Using MIDI cables, connect the OUT of each one to the IN of the other and make sure that both have monitors connected.
● It should now be possible to play the sounds of each keyboard from the other one. It may be that you hear two different timbres playing the same notes if they are set up differently.

☐ **To stop both playing at once**, turn off the LOCAL ON/OFF setting on one of them. Now it will act as a master keyboard and will not play its own sounds, but only the ones from the other keyboard.

☐ Try adding a third device by connecting a sound module's IN socket to a THRU socket on one of the other keyboards.

● Play sounds from the sequence through the module by turning their channels off on the other instruments. This unplayed data will then pass 'thru' to the sound module which can be set up to play it. Use the diagram *below* to help you.

Volume

L R
OUTPUT

VOLUME   **Strings**   ◀▷

Enter

IN   THRU

Volume

PEDAL   IN   OUT   THRU   L   R
OUTPUT

VOLUME   **Saxophone**
● ● ● ● ● ● ● ●
Local: ON   MENU
Bend Mod

Volume

PEDAL   IN   OUT   THRU   L   R
OUTPUT

VOLUME   **Trumpet**   1
● ● ● ● ● ● ● ●
Local: ON   MENU
Bend Mod

CHAPTER 7
THE VIRTUAL STUDIO

COMPUTER PRODUCTION

Computers are now at the heart of most music production. There has been a multimedia revolution, making it possible to manipulate sound, images and video in ways that were unimaginable just a few years ago.

Multimedia software tends to 'model' the real world. To make itself user-friendly it recreates familiar tools and equipment from the original processes.

Music software creates a virtual studio:

● Tracks can be recorded and played back
● Inputs and outputs can be wired together
● Equipment such as compressors, effects units and mixers appear on screen as graphics with moveable faders and switches
● Virtual instruments can be used to perform and record.

You can work creatively entirely within the world of software, until you wish to add some live sound. Then, you will need to connect your equipment (such as a microphone) to the computer using an **audio interface**, which converts analog signals to digital data and back again. The combination of hardware and software used to work in this way is known as a **Digital Audio Workstation (DAW)**. The main parts of a DAW are:

● An audio interface to convert analog signals to digital and back again
● A computer running studio music software.

The balance between hardware and software is wide-ranging. You can use a computer just for recording and playback – or you can do almost everything with software and only use the minimum of hardware to connect everything together. This chapter will cover:

> **FACT**
> **Hardware** refers to the physical components of computers.
>
> **Software** refers to the programs that run on them.

● How to set up and connect together a DAW
● Creating a project in music software
● Recording and editing MIDI data
● Recording and editing audio data.

SETTING UP YOUR DAW

If you want to record from a microphone, guitar or line level into a computer you need a physical connection to the computer. Most computers have built-in sound for a simple microphone input and headphone output, but this is not suitable for high-quality recording.

For high-quality recording, you will need an **audio interface**. This provides the connectivity required, with inputs and outputs in a 'breakout box' and a USB lead joining it to the computer.

A TYPICAL '2 IN/2 OUT' AUDIO AND MIDI INTERFACE

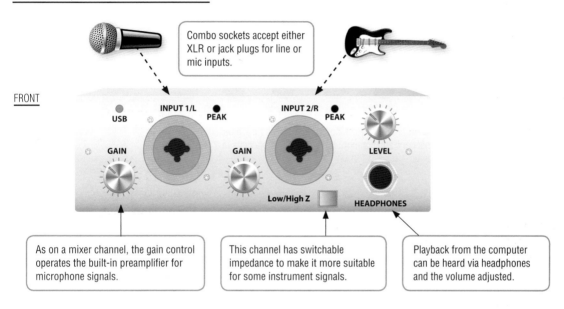

FRONT

Combo sockets accept either XLR or jack plugs for line or mic inputs.

As on a mixer channel, the gain control operates the built-in preamplifier for microphone signals.

This channel has switchable impedance to make it more suitable for some instrument signals.

Playback from the computer can be heard via headphones and the volume adjusted.

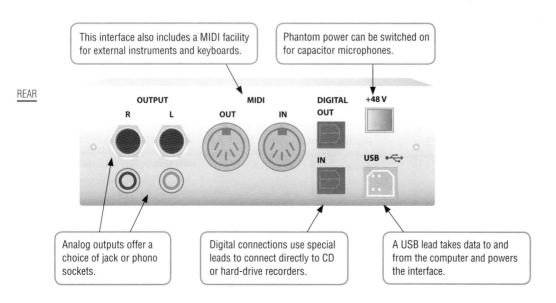

REAR

This interface also includes a MIDI facility for external instruments and keyboards.

Phantom power can be switched on for capacitor microphones.

Analog outputs offer a choice of jack or phono sockets.

Digital connections use special leads to connect directly to CD or hard-drive recorders.

A USB lead takes data to and from the computer and powers the interface.

►MULTI-TRACKING

A small desktop interface with one or two inputs and outputs will allow you to work with MIDI and audio tracks, building up a project step by step. With direct input of guitars and MIDI, you can do most of this in a busy classroom or at home, saving the microphone recording for a quiet moment.

However, if you need to record or play back more tracks simultaneously (perhaps a number of microphones on a drum kit), a larger, studio-quality interface will be needed such as the one shown *below*. These connect to a computer via USB, or sometimes with a card that is fitted inside the computer.

REAR PANEL OF AN 8-INPUT/8-OUTPUT AUDIO INTERFACE

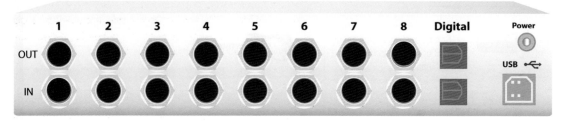

Large interfaces are often rack-mountable, and can be wired to direct inputs and outputs from a mixer.
Similar size interfaces are available for MIDI connections and are more likely to be separate units in a large DAW.

►SOFTWARE CONNECTIONS

Before using your MIDI and audio interfaces, they need to be installed on your computer. Driver software is supplied with the interface, or updated online. The driver is a program that recognises the MIDI or audio equipment and enables other software to use it and to set preferences. It is important to check if a software control panel for your interface is available when it has been installed before using any music software. Sometimes these have faders for the inputs and outputs as well as menus that limit input levels. If these are wrongly set, you may find that signals are not recording or playing back properly. It is possible to use more than one audio interface and to combine their operation, making large numbers of inputs and outputs available to your DAW.

You need to choose the audio interface that you are going to use from within your audio software. This option is usually available within a menu or panel of options. So, if you were using the interface illustrated *above* you would click the option highlighted here:

Most audio software allows the creation of labelled inputs and outputs in the same way that a hardware mixer has a 'main out' or 'control room out'. Once a new input or output bus has been created, you can choose the sockets on your interface that you wish to use for it.

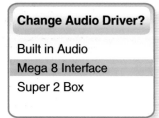

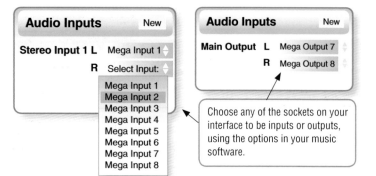

Choose any of the sockets on your interface to be inputs or outputs, using the options in your music software.

CREATING A PROJECT IN MUSIC SOFTWARE

▶ PROJECT-BASED MUSIC

Modern music software usually combines MIDI sequencing with audio recording. You can work with either separately or both at the same time. This may create a number of files which work together as a project.

▶ COMPUTER MUSIC

Digital audio requires a large amount of processing power from a computer as well as significant amounts of storage space for files. If possible, use a separate computer for music work. If that is not practical, avoid running other applications at the same time.

▶ KEEPING IT TOGETHER

Most software will open a dialogue box when you start a new project, offering to use a template or a new, blank file. A **template** is a file to get you started with some tracks and settings already in place. You can make and save your own templates.

You also need to decide where to save the project (also known as the **save path** or **record path**). Any computer-based music project has to be kept in a folder. Within that folder will be the project file (recognisable by the icon of the software you are using) and an additional folder for any audio files. It is essential that you save the project as soon as you create it. Then find the folder on your computer or network and make sure it contains the correct files.

▶ BACKUP

If you need to move your work, you must copy the entire folder. Some software will resave the project in a new location with all the associated files and this is the best option. Always save at least one copy of your project to removable storage every time you finish working.

▶ FILE TYPES

Music software

Any music application will have its own unique file format. This stores all the information about the project and controls the recording and playback of other files. It will have a recognisable icon and file extension (the letters added at the end of the file name, not always visible).

Audio files

Digital audio files store sound as a series of samples, which are themselves numbers. This creates a lot of data and for stereo sound it usually works out at around 10MB (megabytes) per minute. There are different types of audio file and they are usually referred to by their file extensions. Common formats include WAV and AIFF.

MIDI files

When you work with MIDI tracks, the sequencing data is stored in the project file. If you want to use this in another program you need to **export** a MIDI file. This will have the file extension .mid and only contains the MIDI data, excluding all the graphical detail of the program you are using. MIDI files are very small, usually just a few KB (kilobytes).

One file

Every time you record something, however short, a new audio file is created. You could end up with hundreds of files, some of which will not be needed. To finish a project, you need to create a master track that can be played back by any listener. This can be done by recording the mixed output from your project in real time. It can also be created digitally by exporting a final audio file in a suitable format for distibution.

PROJECT FOLDER

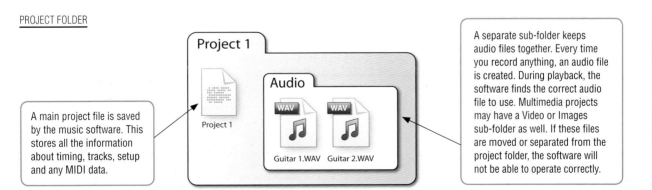

A main project file is saved by the music software. This stores all the information about timing, tracks, setup and any MIDI data.

Project 1

Project 1

Audio

WAV WAV

Guitar 1.WAV   Guitar 2.WAV

A separate sub-folder keeps audio files together. Every time you record anything, an audio file is created. During playback, the software finds the correct audio file to use. Multimedia projects may have a Video or Images sub-folder as well. If these files are moved or separated from the project folder, the software will not be able to operate correctly.

VIEWING A PROJECT

▶ REPRESENTING THE MUSIC

Studio software creates a visual representation of real-world equipment and processes. Each software package has its own way of picturing tracks, equipment and controls, but they all have some basic features in common. In most software, a project has one main window showing the tracks and the timeline. Other windows or panels will show a virtual mixer, instrument or other features as required.

The project window is the starting point for all setting up, recording and playback. Tracks of either audio or MIDI are arranged vertically underneath a timeline – anything vertically aligned will play back at the same time. Whenever something is recorded in a track, a 'part' or 'region' appears. Information about tracks or parts appears when they are selected.

A TYPICAL PROJECT WINDOW

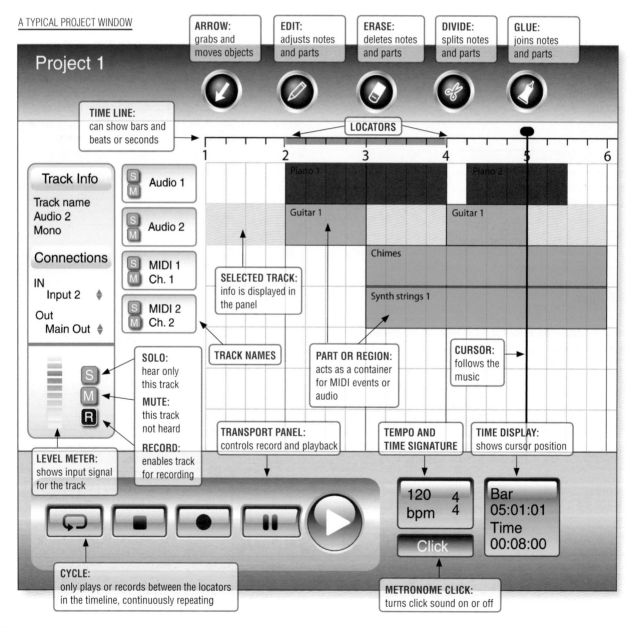

ARROW: grabs and moves objects

EDIT: adjusts notes and parts

ERASE: deletes notes and parts

DIVIDE: splits notes and parts

GLUE: joins notes and parts

Project 1

TIME LINE: can show bars and beats or seconds

LOCATORS

Track Info
Track name
Audio 2
Mono

Connections
IN
    Input 2
Out
    Main Out

SELECTED TRACK: info is displayed in the panel

TRACK NAMES

PART OR REGION: acts as a container for MIDI events or audio

CURSOR: follows the music

SOLO: hear only this track

MUTE: this track not heard

RECORD: enables track for recording

LEVEL METER: shows input signal for the track

TRANSPORT PANEL: controls record and playback

TEMPO AND TIME SIGNATURE

TIME DISPLAY: shows cursor position

Audio 1
Audio 2
MIDI 1 Ch. 1
MIDI 2 Ch. 2

Piano 1
Guitar 1
Piano 2
Guitar 1
Chimes
Synth strings 1

120 bpm   4 4

Click

Bar 05:01:01
Time 00:08:00

CYCLE: only plays or records between the locators in the timeline, continuously repeating

METRONOME CLICK: turns click sound on or off

74

WORKING WITH MIDI

▶ RECORDING AND EDITING A MIDI SEQUENCE

In a hardware sequencer editing can be difficult – they often have a small display and you will need to work through lots of menus and dialogues. In a software sequencer, everything is laid out visually and can be seen in relation to a timeline. The 'parts' or 'regions' that contain MIDI data can be resized, joined or deleted. A variety of editing screens are always available, the most common being a **graphic editor** and a **list editor**. Different programs give these various names, but they are always present in some form within well-known sequencing packages. When a track is selected, relevant information appears and the editors will display the data from that track.

Sequencing is covered in more detail in Chapter 10.

▶ NOTE ENTRY

For realistic results, it is best to play the notes in from a keyboard.

You can do this in small sections or even note by note. Notes can be entered with the mouse if necessary. Sections can be copied and pasted, which can be very useful for drum riffs, choruses and any music that is repeated.

PROJECT WINDOW

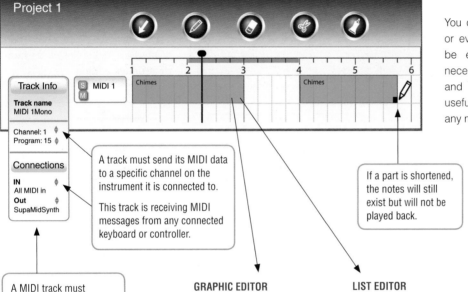

A track must send its MIDI data to a specific channel on the instrument it is connected to.

This track is receiving MIDI messages from any connected keyboard or controller.

If a part is shortened, the notes will still exist but will not be played back.

A MIDI track must connect to an instrument – in this case a software instrument. External MIDI interface outputs would also be shown in this menu.

A keyboard shows the pitch of the notes.

Each note has a velocity which can be seen and edited graphically.

GRAPHIC EDITOR

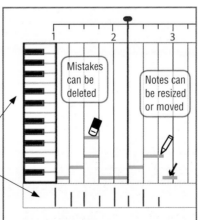

Mistakes can be deleted

Notes can be resized or moved

LIST EDITOR

Bar	Event	Data 1	Data 2	Chn
01:01:01	Program	15		1
01:01:01	CC	7	110	1
01:01:01	CC	10	80	1
01:01:01	Note On	60	100	1
01:02:01	Note Off	60	0	1
01:02:01	Note On	62	70	1
01:03:01	Note Off	62	0	1
01:03:01	Note On	64	70	1
01:04:01	Note Off	64	0	1
01:04:01	Note On	60	50	1
02:01:01	Note Off	60	0	1

The **graphic editor** represents notes as shapes on a time-based grid. The spacing of the grid can be changed, and the notes can be made to snap to the bar or beat. Other data may be represented graphically too, including volume, pan, modulation and all the standard controllers.

In the **list editor** *above*, the time position of events is listed first. Program change, volume and pan settings have been sent at the beginning of the track. They are visible and can be added and changed in the list editor.

▶RECORDING AND EDITING AUDIO

Computer-based studio music began with MIDI. However, towards the end of the 1990s recording digital audio to hard drive became practical and affordable as computers became more powerful, with increased memory and processing power. Audio and MIDI editors both existed separately, but the software companies soon realised the benefits of integrating them. Programs were created that could edit both MIDI and audio data at the same time, and they used the same visual techniques to show MIDI and audio tracks running in parallel. There are many advantages to digital-audio sequencing. It is easy to edit visually – cutting, splicing and overdubbing – and the number of tracks is only limited by the resources of the computer.

▶EDITING

Each section of audio plays back a file from the project folder. If the on-screen part is shortened, cut or joined to another, the original audio is unaffected – the software simply plays back the appropriate part of the file. This is known as **non-destructive editing**.

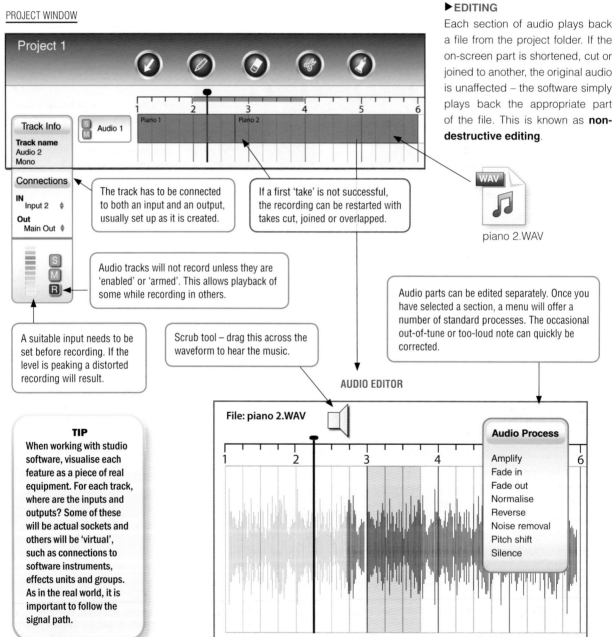

PROJECT WINDOW

Project 1

Track Info
S M Audio 1

Track name
Audio 2
Mono

Connections
IN
Input 2 ⬍
Out
Main Out ⬍

S
M
R

Piano 1   Piano 2

The track has to be connected to both an input and an output, usually set up as it is created.

If a first 'take' is not successful, the recording can be restarted with takes cut, joined or overlapped.

WAV
♫
piano 2.WAV

Audio tracks will not record unless they are 'enabled' or 'armed'. This allows playback of some while recording in others.

Audio parts can be edited separately. Once you have selected a section, a menu will offer a number of standard processes. The occasional out-of-tune or too-loud note can quickly be corrected.

A suitable input needs to be set before recording. If the level is peaking a distorted recording will result.

Scrub tool – drag this across the waveform to hear the music.

AUDIO EDITOR

TIP
When working with studio software, visualise each feature as a piece of real equipment. For each track, where are the inputs and outputs? Some of these will be actual sockets and others will be 'virtual', such as connections to software instruments, effects units and groups. As in the real world, it is important to follow the signal path.

File: piano 2.WAV

1   2   3   4

Audio Process
Amplify
Fade in
Fade out
Normalise
Reverse
Noise removal
Pitch shift
Silence

6

PROJECTS AND SUGGESTIONS

▶ HARDWARE

Modern computers are so powerful that studio software will run on most new models. If you are choosing or building a computer specifically for music software, go for as much internal memory (RAM) as you can. This can be added easily and cheaply to an existing machine. A second hard drive is a good idea too, as the project files can be saved on this while the main drive is kept free for running the programs. A faster processor will give you smoother-running audio and MIDI, with more tracks and processes able to run at the same time.

Noise is another important factor in setting up a computer-based studio. Powerful computers are full of fans and spinning hard drives. Some companies make specialist music computers to deal with these issues. You can also purchase enclosures which surround your computer to cut the noise and keep the temperature stable. Alternatively, you can fit quiet components and fans.

▶ SOFTWARE

There are many well-known music production programs on the market – they all offer more features than most people will use in a lifetime, and all have much in common. To become familiar with a new program, start simply. Experiment on your own, making sure you know how the software connects to the outside world, how to create and edit tracks and other basic operations.

You don't have to spend a fortune getting started with music software. The 'light' versions of most programs are still very powerful and free audio and MIDI editing software is increasingly available online.

▶ TEST YOURSELF

01 What is a driver program for?

02 Name two audio file formats.

03 Which is larger, an audio file or a MIDI file?

04 What does DAW stand for?

05 On average, how much computer storage is needed to record a minute of stereo audio?

06 Name the two common editing screens for MIDI data.

▶ TRY THIS

Get to know the 'workspace' – the visual display you are presented with when you open your studio software. There will be an area for tracks, a transport panel and information panels.
- How do you open, close and move the panels?
- Is there easy access to a mixer or editing screens?

It's worth spending some time finding out about the basics of the program.

Look at the options and templates which are on offer when you click 'New Project'. Where are templates saved and how do you create your own?

Create a new blank project. Add a MIDI track and click on it. When you press a key on your MIDI keyboard, do you see any activity on screen? Check the MIDI inputs and outputs. Every track must connect to an instrument.

Most software has built-in virtual instruments that can be chosen from a list – you should be able to see your MIDI interface in the output menu on the track information panel for connection to 'real' instruments.

Record a few bars by playing the keyboard. A coloured part should appear.
- Try out the tools to lengthen, shorten or cut it.
- Open the part in the graphic or list editor – either by clicking or from a menu.
- Move the notes around, change their length and velocity.
- See if you can add volume or pan controllers graphically.

Create an audio track – mono for a single instrument, stereo if it is to record a keyboard or anything else with left and right outputs.
- In the track information panel, choose an input and output for the track. What do they connect to – sockets on your interface box, a mixer, a patchbay?
- Follow the signal path from the virtual studio to the real one.

Connect a microphone or other sound source to your chosen input.
- When you make some sound, do you see any activity on screen?
- Do you need to press record or a 'monitor' button to see the level coming in?

Experiment with the software and hardware gain until you have a signal that you can check.

Record a few seconds of sound once you have an input working.
- Can you play it back?
- Find the software mixer and adjust volume and panning.

TIP
Getting to know music studio software can be a daunting process – there are so many options. If a manual is not supplied in book form, then it will probably have been installed in the Help menu as a PDF or similar electronic document. The first couple of chapters usually explain the basics and the setting-up. After that, search the documentation every time you are puzzled and browse through it in spare moments.

SECTION 2:
PUTTING IT INTO PRACTICE

CHAPTER 8
RECORDING

GETTING ON TRACK

▶ **GETTING STARTED WITH MULTI-TRACK RECORDING**
Multi-track recording is essentially a three-stage process:

- **Tracking:** recording the individual instruments in turn
- **Mixing:** balancing and panning the parts, adding effects or processing
- **Mastering:** creating the final stereo track, ready for distribution.

This chapter will focus on the first stage: how to set up and record individual instruments. Mixing and mastering are covered in **Chapter 9**.

The tracking stage can be accomplished using a multi-track recorder or a computer – the latter is by far the most common option now.

When using a computer to record, signals have to be sent in and out of it using an **audio interface**. A **hardware mixer** is also necessary to act as a hub for all the equipment. It provides phantom power for the microphones, and allows the signals to be sent to the performers in the studio and to the recording engineer in the control room. It also controls the levels sent to and from the computer for recording and playback.

The mixing and mastering stages can take place entirely within computer software or using a combination of hardware mixer, outboard equipment and software.

▶ **GETTING READY**
Before starting a recording project, you need to think about how to approach it. In most cases, it is best to rehearse the piece thoroughly all together before recording, especially when the project forms part of a course that is going to be examined and you are playing the parts of both engineer and producer. The more preparation you do, the more likely it is that you will achieve a successful outcome. So, before you start:

- Make sure you are familiar with the song
- Choose and book your musicians
- Print out the scores (lyrics, guitar chords, drum patterns and so on)
- If possible, give the musicians scores in advance to practise from
- Rehearse the song all together.

▶ **WHO IS GOING TO START?**
If your song uses drums, they are usually recorded first. There is an important musical issue here – the drummer needs to know the piece really well and has to be able to play it while imagining the contributions of other musicians. If the piece starts with just guitar, say, or piano, then it may be best to start with that. You don't have to record the whole song, just enough to lead the drums in. Sometimes it is best to begin with an instrument that plays throughout the piece instead of the drums and of course, not every piece has a drum part!

> **GUIDE TRACK**
> A guide track is a rough recording of a piece which is used to help musicians keep in time when multi-tracking their parts. To create a guide track, record the whole piece (or at least the important parts) with just a couple of microphones in front of the musicians. Make sure that it is strictly in time and that the melody is clearly heard.

▶ **SETTING THE TEMPO**
To set and maintain a consistent tempo, use a click track. A click track acts like a metronome that musicians can listen to through their headphones. To create a click track, work out the tempo by playing along with the click of your recording software. Keep changing the BPM (beats per minute) setting until you match the opening tempo. Be aware of any changes later on in the song.

SETTING UP SOFTWARE

Start by creating a new project in your software. This lets you map out the recording visually, so you can see what connections will be needed. Add the number of audio tracks that you need and label them each with the name of the instrument you are recording to it. Make sure that the project is safely saved in its own folder.

Every track will need an input and an output:

Track output: while recording, set all the tracks to use the same stereo output. This means you will be able to hear a balanced playback of recorded material while recording new tracks.

Track input: this should represent a socket on the back of your interface, which is connected to a direct output (tape send) from one of the channels on your mixer.

Timing: set the tempo and time signature on the transport bar. The metronome (click) may have separate settings for sound and volume. Make sure this is using the same output as the tracks and start with a low volume so that it isn't uncomfortable when you are setting up the foldback for performers.

▶TRACKS

The number of tracks you can record at the same time will be decided by the number of inputs on your interface. If you are working in a well equipped studio, you may have eight or 16 inputs, or even more.

For most projects, you are unlikely to need more than eight inputs at once unless you are recording a band playing altogether or you have several microphones around a drum kit.

Most of the time you will be recording just one track with one microphone although you may need two or three for some instruments. It is possible to record drums well with between two and four microphones but it's also common to use more. In the software project window (*right*), only four inputs are needed.

TRACK SET-UP FOR A TYPICAL RECORDING

SOFTWARE PROJECT WINDOW

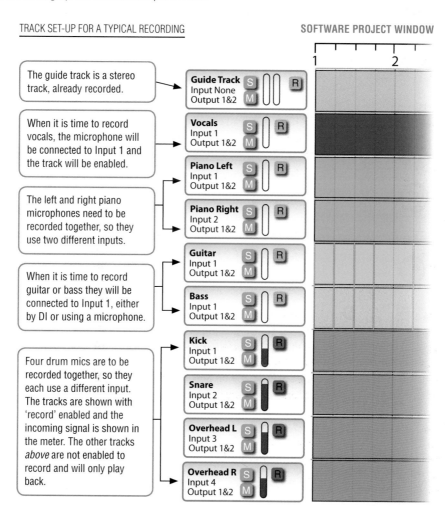

The guide track is a stereo track, already recorded.

Guide Track — Input None — Output 1&2

When it is time to record vocals, the microphone will be connected to Input 1 and the track will be enabled.

Vocals — Input 1 — Output 1&2

The left and right piano microphones need to be recorded together, so they use two different inputs.

Piano Left — Input 1 — Output 1&2

Piano Right — Input 2 — Output 1&2

When it is time to record guitar or bass they will be connected to Input 1, either by DI or using a microphone.

Guitar — Input 1 — Output 1&2

Bass — Input 1 — Output 1&2

Four drum mics are to be recorded together, so they each use a different input. The tracks are shown with 'record' enabled and the incoming signal is shown in the meter. The other tracks *above* are not enabled to record and will only play back.

Kick — Input 1 — Output 1&2

Snare — Input 2 — Output 1&2

Overhead L — Input 3 — Output 1&2

Overhead R — Input 4 — Output 1&2

▶INPUT PATH

Now you have set up a project in your software, you need to route audio signals to your tracks from your hardware. If you are working in a studio that is already set up, you need to check the path that the signal follows from studio to audio track. If you are setting up from scratch, make sure that your direct outputs are connected to the tracks on which you want to record.

▶SIGNAL PATH

1 This microphone is connected to Channel 1. There may be a wallbox or patchbay to connect it.

2 The direct output from the channel sends the mic signal to the audio interface. On larger mixers this may need to be chosen from a bank of switches.

3 The interface accepts the audio signal and digitises it.

4 Digital information from all the inputs is sent to the computer via a USB or similar connection.

5 The track input needs to correspond with the audio interface input.

6 The signal will only be accepted if the track is enabled. An input level meter will show that the signal is coming in.

▶SETTING UP

1 Press the PFL button. The signal will now bypass the fader and be heard through the control room output.

2 Adjust the channel gain until a healthy signal is seen on the main output level meters – as high as possible without going into the red/peaking. Release the PFL button.

3 With the fader at 0 there should now be a healthy signal with some room to move up or down.

4 Record enable the track – there will be a button for this. The software may have an input level meter too, on the track and/or in its own mixer.

5 On some mixers, each channel has a button to send the signal to the main mix – this will need to be pressed to hear the incoming signal through the monitors. The sound goes to the direct outputs for recording regardless of whether the mix button is pressed.

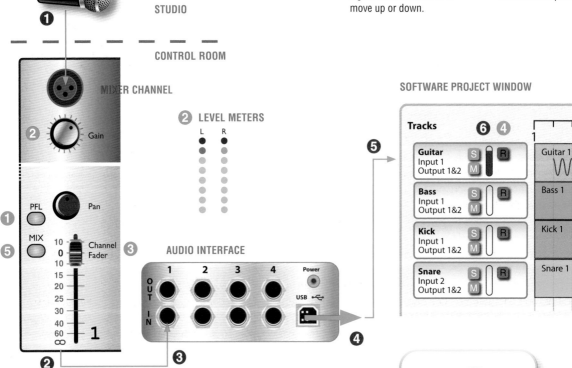

DIRECT OUTPUT
This is usually a socket on the back of the mixer.
Sometimes group outputs double as direct outputs.

TIP
If the signal fails to appear in the track, check the audio interface software settings, including levels.

SETTING UP HARDWARE

▶ OUTPUT PATH

With an audio signal coming into your software, you now need to work out how to listen to it. There are two main factors to consider. You need to hear the performer(s) whose signals are coming into the mixer and the playback of any previously recorded tracks. The performers also need to hear themselves along with the playback – their performance will be greatly helped by hearing a suitably balanced and panned mix in their headphones.

To hear playback from the computer, the tracks need to send a mixed signal to a stereo pair of outputs.

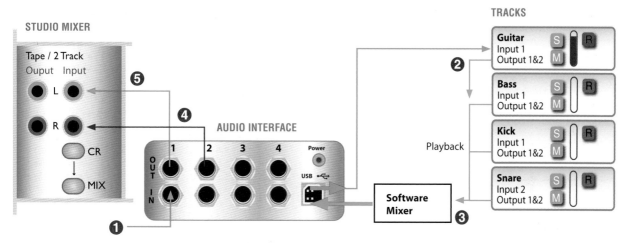

① A guitar signal is sent into Input 1

② If a track is record enabled, the incoming signal will be sent to the track output as well as being recorded

③ All the output signals go through a software mixer, so you can balance and pan what you are hearing without affecting any tracks that are being recorded

④ The output signals are sent to the audio interface via USB or similar computer connection. Here, all these signals are routed to Outputs 1 and 2

⑤ Both the playback and the incoming guitar signal return to the mixer through the 2 Track input and can be heard through the main mix and/or control room outputs.

Note: if the incoming signal(s) are also being sent directly to the mix from their input channels, you will hear them twice, once as they come in to the mixer and again as they return via the playback. To avoid this, once channel levels have been set and the track enabled, release the Mix button on each channel. The incoming signal will then be sent directly to record via the direct output and will be heard along with the playback.

> **TIP**
> Any stereo input, or two mono channels can be used to listen to the playback. Care has to be taken, however, not to set up a feedback loop between inputs and outputs.

ALL MIXED UP

If you are using a computer to record, you have two mixers at your disposal – one in the real world controlling the equipment and setting levels for inputs, and one in your recording software controlling the output levels of each track.

If your hardware mixer has enough channels with direct returns, you can play back each track separately and monitor it as you record.

Most of us don't have this sort of facility available, let alone an audio interface that will cater for the large number of tracks that are built up during a recording. In most situations of home, school or college based recording, the most straightforward way of working is to use the software mixer for playback and to keep the output as a simple stereo pair.

▶ FOLDBACK

When recording, performers need to hear both themselves and previously-recorded material. To do this you need to supply performers with an audio feed to their headphones – this is known as **foldback**. If more than one person is playing, they will each need a headphone feed and the signal will have to be split. This can be achieved with a main foldback amplifier followed by a splitter. Alternatively, more sophisticated amplifier/splitters are available that give each user their own volume control.

▶ HEADPHONES

Open headphones: allow sound through to the ears from outside, which for some people makes playing more comfortable. However, these can spill sound, which may reach a microphone and be picked up on the recording, so they need to be used with care.

Closed headphones: give a greater sense of isolation and prevent spill. When these are used, it is particularly important that you send the performer a mix they can play along with comfortably.

HEADPHONE AMPLIFIER/SPLITTER

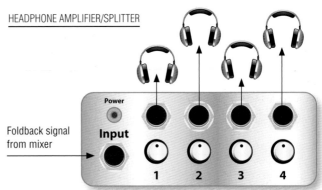

Foldback signal from mixer

FOLDBACK SOURCE

Now that music software offers us the use of a virtual mixer in which the playback signals can be balanced and panned, the control-room playback is usually the best signal to send to performers too. This may be possible from the headphone socket or by taking the left and right outputs to an amplifier. You may need to use an adapter and a splitter if these sockets are also feeding your control room monitors. Pre-fade auxiliary outputs can be also used to create a foldback mix, but it will be in mono. This may not suit performers playing along with it, and it may be difficult to combine this with playback from previous tracks.

Whatever the source of foldback, it is important to check that the levels are suitable to connect to amplifiers. Headphone outputs may be too high for some amplifiers to accept without distortion.

MIXER OUTPUT

The headphone output from the mixer output section offers a possible source of foldback signal too, and can be sent to a splitter. If you use the control room or main mix outputs for foldback they will need to be amplified.

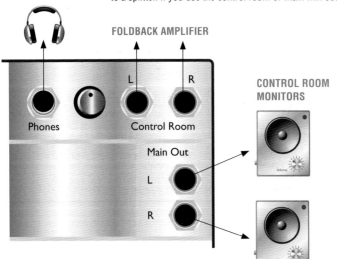

FOLDBACK AMPLIFIER

CONTROL ROOM MONITORS

TIP

If you are sending the playback from your computer back to two channels on your mixing desk, you may be able to route these to a group output for foldback (as well as to the control room for monitoring). If you do not have extra group outputs, use the main mix outputs for control room monitors and control room output for foldback – the recording tracks are using direct outputs, so your main mix is likely to be unused during tracking.

On large studio mixers, dedicated foldback outputs will be available to which direct returns, control room or other signals can be routed.

GETTING READY TO RECORD

The first thing you need to consider is where to record. If working at home, you will need to set up a suitable space. Ideally, recording equipment should be in a separate room from performers, or at least screened in some way to stop noise spilling into microphones. Computer noise, in particular, is a real problem if it is in the recording space. If using a garage or shed, you will need to do some soundproofing both to stop noise affecting your recordings and also to keep the neighbours happy. This is a big topic all of its own, and if you are going to create a home studio some research will be necessary.

With a little care, good recordings can be made in classrooms and improvised studios. Avoid rooms with low ceilings, and keep instruments and microphones away from walls, corners and the centre of the room. Drawing curtains together will help, as will carefully placing blankets and duvets over hard surfaces to damp the sound reflections. Have a good listen to the instrument in the room – make sure that loud playing doesn't cause any rattles. If it sounds terrible live, then the chances are it will sound terrible when recorded and you may need to use another room.

▶ ROOM NOISE

On playback, you may hear rumbles and low-level noises which you were unaware of when listening or recording. Bumps on microphone stands, loose floorboards and noise travelling through the floor can be picked up by sensitive microphones. Some microphones have a roll-off switch (see **Chapter 3**) which can help with this, but it is best to avoid it in the first place with a few precautions:

- Make sure the central pole of a microphone stand does not touch the floor – tighten all the segments firmly and make sure the rubber feet are in place.
- If recording a guitar amplifier, lift it off the floor – use a chair or block to stand it on.
- Put a drum kit on a piece of carpet – this will cut down floor noise and prevent it from moving when played.
- Use suspension mounts for vocal microphones.

▶ TUNING

When playing as a group, it is normal to tune up together. When recording one track at a time, it's easy to forget that this needs to be checked. It is essential that whoever plays the first track is correctly in tune, and that those who follow tune to the same reference and double-check against previously recorded tracks. Electronic tuners are very useful for this.

If there is a piano in the song, then all other other instruments **must** tune to it first. Piano tuning is subtly different to that of guitars, and mixing them in a recording can be difficult. This is a musical issue that you need to be aware of in a multi-track project. Avoid long delays between tracks involving piano, as its tuning is likely to change.

KEYBOARD TUNING

Its easy to assume that electronic instruments are always in tune – however, they do sometimes 'drift'. Check for a reset facility on your keyboard – some also have a 'master tune' option in the menu allowing you to nudge the pitch up or down in cents (hundredths of a tone).

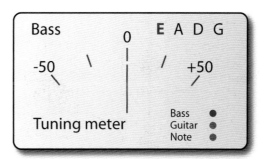

Tuning meter

▶ ACOUSTIC

Depending on the design and the type of strings, acoustic guitars vary in the volume of sound they produce. Their sound will also be affected by the space in which they are played, so listen carefully in the room. If it is too dead, this may be caused by carpet – try placing the guitarist's chair on a sheet of board which will reflect sound upwards.

▶ MICROPHONE CHOICE

Small-diaphragm capacitor microphones work well with guitars. They have the sensitivity to capture the guitar's full dynamic range as well as its timbre, which is rich in overtones.

▶ MICROPHONE PLACEMENT

Start by pointing the microphone at the end of the fretboard. Avoid pointing the microphone straight into the sound hole or directly on the frets. If the guitar is being strummed with a pick, angle the microphone away from the pick position or move it slightly further away. A common problem with guitar recordings is that the clicking sound of strumming is too dominant. A second microphone about halfway up the frets will give a stereo effect – when mixing, you can balance and pan the two sounds.

> **TIP**
> Get an assistant to hold a microphone and move it around in front of the guitar while you listen in the control room. When you have found the optimum position, hold still and set up a microphone stand.

▶ ELECTRIC AND BASS

There are two ways to record an electric guitar or bass: using DI or by recording a guitar amplifier with a microphone.

1. Direct recording, either straight into your mixer or via a DI box, will give a clean sound with a strong signal. An effects pedal or software can be used to imitate the sound of different amps or your favourite effects.

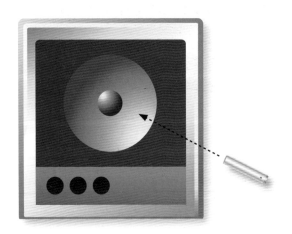

2. For **recording a guitar amplifier**, use dynamic instrument microphones.

Try placing the microphone slightly off-centre and a few inches away from the amplifier's speaker (shown *left*). Experiment with distance from the amplifier and from the edge of the speaker cone – generally, moving towards the edge will dull the sound. Unless you are seeking a particular sound, small amplifiers will work well and there is no need to use a high volume while recording.

Using a combination of direct input and recording the amplifier can also work well.

RECORDING PIANO

For a multi-track recording a grand piano sound can be captured with two close microphones, one above the higher strings and one above the mid/lower strings. If possible, remove the lid to give more room. Sturdy microphone stands will be necessary – they must not touch the piano body.

▶ MICROPHONE CHOICE

A pair of dynamic instrument microphones will give a harder sound which may suit some styles of music. For a fuller sound that will capture the wide frequency range of the piano with all its overtones, small diaphragm capacitor microphones are a good choice. These are likely to be directional (cardioid), so make sure that a sufficient range of notes is picked up by each microphone or try omni-directional microphones if they are available.

▶ MICROPHONE PLACEMENT

Place the higher microphone near the front, moving up from middle C to the range you are likely to be playing in. The other microphone can be placed in an equivalent position below middle C, or further towards the bass end, depending on the music.

At some point the strings cross, so an alternative is to move the lower microphone to the foot of the casing where the lower strings are exposed.

Experiment with positioning to avoid the 'hole in the middle' effect. With the lid removed completely, it's easier to experiment with vertical placement – if the microphones are very close to the strings, you may not hear the full range of notes evenly. One good way to test this is to ask the pianist to play the keyboard from one extreme to the other while you listen for an even capture of the sound.

> **TIP**
> Beware of pedal noise – not just from the pedal itself, but also from the dampers which are lifted up and down just inside the piano case. You may need to move the microphones back from the dampers, or angle them away slightly, to minimise this.

GRAND PIANO

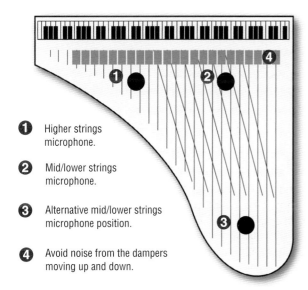

❶ Higher strings microphone.

❷ Mid/lower strings microphone.

❸ Alternative mid/lower strings microphone position.

❹ Avoid noise from the dampers moving up and down.

UPRIGHT PIANO

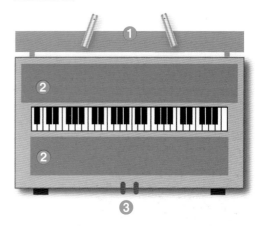

❶ Microphones can point into the open lid, capturing high and low strings.

❷ Panels can be removed, giving more scope for microphone placement.

❸ Avoid noise from the pedals.

87

RECORDING DRUMS

There are as many ways of recording a drum kit as there are recordings of drum kits. Everyone has their favourite method. Only practice and experience will lead you to your ideal recorded drum sound. One relatively simple way to begin is by using four microphones:

- Two above the kit to capture the overall sound
- One to reinforce the kick drum
- One for the snare.

You can go on to add microphones for individual toms, cymbals and any number of extras – drums are sometimes surrounded by a forest of microphone stands!

▶ OVERHEADS
These can be used in two ways: as a 'stereo pair' recording the whole kit or as two microphones capturing approximately half of the kit each.

▶ MICROPHONE CHOICE
Drum microphones can be purchased in sets and this is a great way to get started. The two overhead mics will be small-diaphragm capacitor models, so you will need to give them some phantom power. Snare, tom and kick drum mics are always dynamic and specially made to suit the drums' frequency ranges and levels of sound. Sets often include clips which fit directly onto the drums. If you are not using a set, a specialist kick-drum microphone is a good idea with dynamic instrument mics for snare and toms, and capacitor microphones for overheads

▶ POSITIONING

1 Overheads do not have to be the same height or evenly spaced – set them up to capture a suitable balance of instruments on each side of the kit. Experimentation is the key to success.

2 Snare drum microphones can be clipped onto the rim or supported with a stand. Angle it down towards the head and away from the hi-hat to avoid spill. Listen carefully to the sound – too much ring can be damped with a cloth taped to the head, specialist gel or circular dampers.

4 Extra microphones can be placed over the toms.

3 A kick drum mic can be placed inside the drum through a hole in the rear head, if your drum has one. Alternatively, it can be placed just outside the hole or even on the beater side.

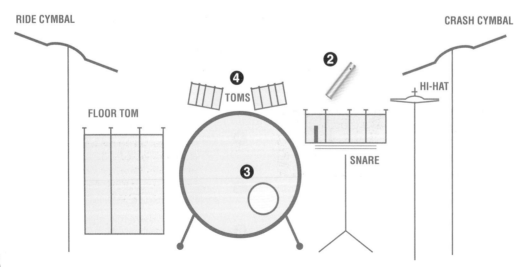

SETTING UP DRUMS

▶ SPACE

Drum recordings will be affected by the room in which the kit is set up. The sound levels from a drum set are high and will be reflected from the walls, ceiling and floor of a lively room. It is difficult to change a whole room, so if you don't like the sound, it may be best to move to a carpeted, quieter room for this session. If that is not possible, putting the kit onto a rug may help and hanging blankets or duvets on the walls will reduce the room sound. Cymbal sounds especially will bounce from the ceiling, so you may need to put some acoustic tiles above the kit too. You may want to record with lots of ambient sound, but if you do, give some careful thought to what else is going into your mix. If other instruments are recorded with different room sounds, they may not work well together.

▶ MAINTENANCE

A drum kit contains a lot of moving parts which can be very noisy. Before starting your session, check that there are no squeaks or rattles. Drum heads need tuning and tensioning – a slack drum head will affect your recording and that sound cannot be fixed later by processing.

> Hopefully the drummer will be able to check and tune the kit – if not, ask for help from a drum teacher or more experienced player.

▶ KIT SOUND

Levels need to be set carefully before recording drums. Ask your drummer to play round the whole kit while you listen to the overheads, with them panned some way to left and right. Can you hear everything in the kit clearly – would the sound of the overheads be sufficient on their own? The overheads are the main source for the sound of cymbals and toms (unless you have added extra microphones). Adjust the gain until the level is strong without peaking.

▶ KICK AND SNARE

When you are happy with the overall kit sound, listen to the kick drum on its own.
- Make sure the loudest hits will not push the channel level into the red.
- Check the character of the sound – if it is not how you want it before you record, then it won't be any better after you have recorded it.
- Make sure that the snare drum is not ringing too much and that the sound is as bright (or not) as you want it to be.

Finally, check that your drummer can hear the click or guide track clearly as well as their own sound. Closed headphones are especially useful here, but care must be taken not to bring levels up to the point where someone's hearing could be damaged.

▶ RECORDING KEYBOARDS

If you are using a keyboard, synthesiser or MIDI sound, it can be input directly to the mixer. A stereo channel is ideal for this (in both hardware and software) unless you want to experiment with panning, in which case you will need two mono channels. With line-level signals, the volume should be set quite high on the instrument. If it is low, the gain on the mixer will need to be brought up and this will also amplify any noise in the circuit.

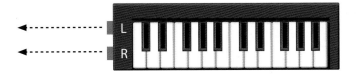

> **TIP**
> Direct-input instruments can often be performed in the control room, saving space and time and making communication quicker and easier.

Vocals are usually the last track(s) recorded and sit prominently in the mix of any recording. The space in which they are recorded is very important. Small rooms with parallel, hard walls are least suitable for vocal recording.

Generally, vocals are recorded dry with reverberation added at the mixing stage. If you have to record in a room that sounds 'boxy' it is especially important to cut reflections from behind and above the singer. Old duvets and blankets work well and can be stuck to walls with strong gaffer tape (although you may damage paintwork when you remove the tape, so choose your location carefully). It is worth having a few acoustic foam tiles available which you can tape to the ceiling. Ideally, use an acoustic booth – a purpose built box into which you put your singer and microphone – or an acoustic shield which curves around the singer on a stand in front of them.

> As with drums, you may choose to record some of the room sound as well. But you do have to keep in mind whether this will fit with the rest of the tracks that you have recorded and whether it will make it difficult to add any effects later.

▶ FOLDBACK

Singing along with pre-recorded tracks in headphones can be difficult. In the foldback, the singer's voice must be prominent. It often helps to add a little reverb from the software playback mixer. This will not be recorded, but will help the singer feel part of the performance.

▶ MICROPHONE CHOICE

Large-diaphragm, cardioid capacitor microphones are the most popular choice for vocal recording. Cardioid patterns are most commonly used, being focused to the front, although the sound they capture can be affected by room reflections and you need to be aware of the proximity effect (see **Chapter 3**). If you have a switchable pattern microphone available, try using it with the omni setting. This will give a natural, full sound and help to avoid 'boxy' effects provided you can control the sound reflections from around the room.

> If you are going to invest in good quality equipment, buying the best microphone you can afford for vocals must be top of the list.

▶ POSITIONING

The most important factor when recording vocals is to keep the distance between singer and microphone as constant as possible. A stable microphone stand, shock mount and separate pop shield are essential. Movement from the singer, rustling clothing and jewellery, knocks on the stand or tapping feet all have the potential to ruin a performance. To keep the singer in place after a break between takes, put some tape on the floor to mark their standing position. Start with the singer about 20cm from the microphone, adjusting the position as necessary. If lyrics are needed, put them on a music stand at eye level, or slightly above, so that the singer does not keep tilting their head down or to one side (make sure the music stand is not affecting the sound).

RECORDING PROCESS

▶ ONE PART OR MORE?

Many recording projects work through the instruments one by one. You don't have to work like this, though, and can record some parts together (most commonly drums, bass and perhaps rhythm guitar) before layering other parts on afterwards. The advantages of this are that you will have a quick start to the project, and the musicians will benefit from the security that working together as a group brings. However, if you are preparing a project for a course or exam, keep in mind that you may be required to record as many parts separately as possible.

If you need flexibility afterwards to balance and pan the sounds then the instruments will have to be very well separated while recording, using acoustic screens, careful microphone placement or even putting them in separate rooms. Direct recording can of course take place in a control room and won't spill any sound into other microphones.

▶ TRACKS, TAKES AND RETAKES

- Before recording, allow a few seconds of silence
- Don't rush for the stop button, wait to let all the reverberation die away and then for a few seconds longer
- Make the takes as long as possible – it's worth going right through a piece the first time, even with mistakes, just to get the feel of the music.

If you need to record something again, you can just repeat a section and with computer-based recording this is easier than ever. Most software will simply record a new take over the top of the previous one without deleting anything, but check the settings first to make sure.

Alternatively, you can record retakes onto new, parallel tracks. When you have finished, you will need to edit the various takes into a comp – a composite of the sections you are happy with.

▶ DROP OR PUNCH

When re-recording a section of a piece, look for a suitable point to start such as the beginning of a phrase or section. Cutting-off breath sounds and reverberation will sound unnatural, so it is essential to time the entry and exit of a retake carefully. Most recording software (and multi-track machines) offer automatic **drop-in** recording, sometimes called punch in. This allows you to start playback at any point, automatically switching to record mode (drop-in) at a point set in the timeline and back to playback at another set point (drop-out). This helps to achieve a natural transition, as the performance will already be underway when recording begins at the drop-in point.

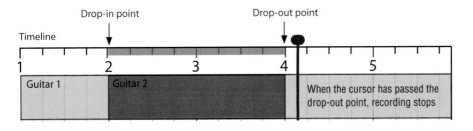

> **TIP**
> Make notes about each session or track including date, time, performer, equipment used (especially microphones), effects, processing and any problems encountered. These will be invaluable later in the project, especially if your work is being assessed as part of a course.

▶ MAKING SURE

Play back at least some of each take when tracking – don't just rely on the appearance of the waveform on screen. Make sure that the takes have similar levels and sound quality and are free of 'peaks'. Digital sound will always distort if levels get too high. If in doubt, record again rather than risk having to recall the performer for another session.

RECORDING ORCHESTRAL INSTRUMENTS

You may wish to include wind, brass, strings or percussion into your multi-track project. Microphone choice and placement for any instrument requires some thought and experimentation. All instruments produce a range of notes plus overtones in various frequency bands. They will sound different as you move around them – just putting a microphone directly in front of the instrument is not necessarily the best idea. A little distance is helpful to capture its full sound. Place the microphone too close and you will hear noisy breathing, bowing or clattering of valves and keys.

▶STRINGS

As with guitars, some reflective surfaces, such as a wooden floor, can help the sound. Too dry or small a room can deaden the sound too much. Other points to remember:

- Cellists will always be seated, and it helps to ask a violin or viola player to sit down too as this will prevent too much moving around.
- Listen carefully to the instrument in the room and try moving a microphone round while someone listens in the control room to choose the best position.
- As well as listening from the front, a microphone position that is looking over the shoulder from behind and above is worth trying.

▶BRASS, WIND AND PERCUSSION

Loud instruments such as trumpets and trombones sound best when recorded with the microphone slightly off-axis from the bell. This can be to one side, above or below. Avoid pointing the microphone into the bell – it is likely to produce a harsh sound with unwanted noise.

The sound of a woodwind instrument is largely projected from the body and the area around the keys. Angle the microphone from above or to one side rather than at the end of the instrument. With flute, oboe and clarinet, an over-the-shoulder approach is worth experimenting with.

Tuned percussion can be recorded in much the same way as a piano, with two microphones for higher and lower pitches placed above the notes.

▶MICROPHONE CHOICE

Distance and volume are major factors in microphone choice. Brass instruments produce very high levels of sound and dynamic instrument microphones must be used in very close proximity, if that is the sound you need. Otherwise, the frequency range and characteristics of instruments determine the choice of microphone. A large diaphragm, cardioid capacitor microphone will suit many instruments, especially strings. For others (such as woodwind), a more focussed, smaller microphone may be more suitable. Experiment with the range of microphones available to you to find the best combination.

COMPRESSION, EQ AND EFFECTS

These can all be added at the mixing stage. If you compress, filter or add an effect to a sound while tracking, it will be permanently recorded and limit your choices later on. For very strong, variable dynamics such as from a trumpet or some wayward singers, mild compression while recording can help to avoid peaks. The track can be further compressed later as necessary. EQ and effects can be added in the foldback mix to help the performance, but are best left unrecorded so that more flexibility is available later on.

QUICK SET-UP FOR ALL INSTRUMENTS

- Set up a music stand at the normal distance and height for the instrument
- Put a microphone stand behind the music stand
- Raise the mic stand up, so that the microphone is pointing down at the player from just above the music stand.

STEREO RECORDING

Two microphones can be used together to capture a stereo 'image' of ambient sound (the sound within a space) such as a group of instrumentalists, orchestra or choir. For some instruments, such as piano, drum overheads or tuned percussion, a stereo recording offers an alternative to close microphone techniques. There are many ways of recording in stereo, the two most common being **spaced pair** and **coincident pair** – both of which can be used together with 'spot' microphones to enhance the sound of particular instruments.

Microphones are positioned evenly either side of a central line through the performing stage. Small adjustments can make a big difference to the final result.

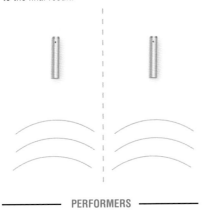

PERFORMERS

Microphone capsules are set at an angle of 90° and as close together as possible. As the microphones are effectively collecting sound from the opposite side of the room, panning has to be adjusted so that the stereo field is not reversed.

PERFORMERS

▶ SPACED PAIR

A sound reaches each of the microphones at a slightly different time. These minute differences are enough for our brains to interpret as a stereo sound field.

Omnidirectional microphones are most commonly used for spaced positioning. They have a natural response and are able to collect the full ambience of the space. Cardioid microphones can also be used, although the already difficult decisions about spacing become even more so.

Spaced stereo recording can be very rewarding when succesful but does have disadvantages: a hole in the middle of the stereo field is a frequent problem, as is 'image shift' when a performer seems to move from one side to the other. Spaced signals do not work well when summed to mono, as the two signals can occasionally cancel each other out. Each situation is different and positioning is crucial to success.

A spaced pair is also sometimes known as an A–B pair.

▶ COINCIDENT PAIR

The stereo effect is created by the differences in level encountered by each microphone for the same sound. Cardioid patterns are normally used, set at 90° to each other a few meters away from performers and raised quite high.

A coincident pair can be very effective as drum overheads either behind a kit or in front of it in the studio. A pair of microphones can be used similarly outside a piano, marimba or other tuned percussion for a stereo effect. Also known as an X–Y pair, a coincident pair is less tricky to set up than spaced recording. The stereo image will be focussed and stable and summing the tracks to mono is not a problem.

There are many variations on these two basic stereo techniques, using different numbers of microphones, angles and distances.

CHAPTER 9
MIXING AND MASTERING

MIXING

Mixing is the process of balancing and panning tracks, adding effects or processing.
Mastering is the process of finalising the product from the mix, creating a stereo track ready for distribution.

▶ GETTING READY TO MIX

When all the tracking is complete, the first and most important step is to save everything and back it up – make a separate copy of the whole project stored separately from the studio computer. As you continue to work on the mix, save continuously and back up at the end of every session, labelling the backups with the date.

Mixing tracks requires a suitable space to work in, concentration and a fresh start. So:

- Resist the urge to start playing with the tracks as soon as the players have left.
- Clear up, put everything away and have a break – start the mixing as a separate process.

SPACE

If you are lucky enough to be working in a purpose-built studio space, hopefully the design and acoustics of the room will be helpful. If setting up your own workspace, care must be taken with the layout and acoustic treatment:

- Small rooms with hard, parallel walls are best avoided. The room doesn't need to be completely 'dead' but lots of unwanted sound reflection will affect your judgement of balance and spatial awareness.
- Ceiling reflections can also be a problem – these can be helped by the addition of sound absorbent tiles.

MONITOR ❶

MONITOR

COMPUTER SCREEN

MIXER OR CONTROL SURFACE

COMPUTER KEYBOARD

❷ LISTENING POSITION

❶ Near-field monitors are used for mixing. These are designed to be listened to close-up and have a flatter frequency response than consumer systems, meaning that you can hear across the frequency range evenly. These are another high priority in any studio budget.

❷ The monitors and the listener need to be in a triangular formation, as close to evenly spaced as possible. Some monitors have lights built in to them to help you line them up. Monitors should be on stands rather than rested on a desk or console, and are usually designed to be upright rather than laid on their sides.

Monitors should not be fixed in the corner of a room and should be away from walls. If possible, avoid having the whole listening set-up centred in the room.

TIP
For more on the basics of mixing, see **Chapter 5**.

EDITING

Each track will need some individual attention before you can start mixing properly. The first thing to check for is unwanted noise. For example, a singer may make unwanted noises in gaps between words or sounds – these need to be cut out, but be careful not to lose the natural decay of the sound at the end of the last note. A very short fade out will help to make smooth endings to sections and this can usually be added from a menu or with a tool.

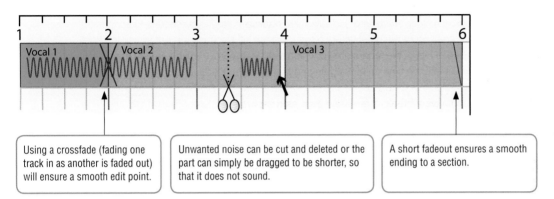

Using a crossfade (fading one track in as another is faded out) will ensure a smooth edit point.

Unwanted noise can be cut and deleted or the part can simply be dragged to be shorter, so that it does not sound.

A short fadeout ensures a smooth ending to a section.

If you have retakes, you need to audition them to decide which ones to keep and where to edit them together. Music software is becoming more sophisticated with every version, and some programs automate this process to the point where you just have to select regions with the mouse and they will form a 'comp'. If working manually, you will need to cut and splice chosen sections, making sure that auto crossfade is switched on or adding crossfades yourself. Clumsy edits will result in audible clicks and changes in level – both of which need to be kept in mind when tracking and editing.

▶LEVELS

Hopefully you will have recorded to a strong level. If you find that some sections are too quiet, this can create problems mixing and some adjustment can be made using the audio editing facilities of your software.

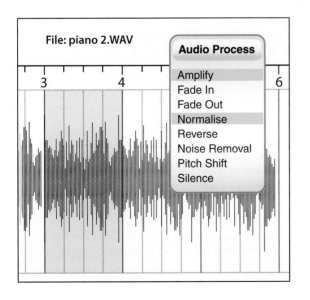

▶GAIN

With a section of the waveform selected, you can apply some amplification (sometimes labelled gain) to increase the level. Too much gain may bring up background noise as well, so some compromise may be necessary. If a lot of adjustment is needed, it may be better to re-record the track. Gain/amplification processing can also be used to reduce the level of a section of audio.

▶NORMALISATION

Digital audio is stored as numerical information. During normalisation, the processor finds the loudest samples and calculates the difference between them and the loudest possible levels. The difference is then added to all samples, bringing everything up as high as possible without peaking.

CHAPTER 9 MIXING AND MASTERING

Having checked and edited individual parts, you now have to decide the order in which to mix them. There are infinite ways of doing this, but the most common methods are:

- Building up an accompanying mix for melody/vocal parts (which are added last)
- Establishing a level and sound for the vocal/melody and then mixing around it
- Listening to everything for a while and starting to adjust the balance
- Mixing as you record, getting fairly close to the sound you want while tracking and adjusting it afterwards.

It is possible, of course, to work in any order that suits you. A mix tends to evolve over several sessions, often revisiting previous ideas and gradually refining the sound. However you choose to work, you need to keep in mind the overall level of the mix and avoid getting to the point where a track will not 'fit' because it is not possible to get low or high enough in level to balance. If lots of the faders are very high and headroom is limited, or you are having to pull many of the tracks well down, it may be time to think again and make a fresh start.

It is a good idea to listen to some commercial tracks that will act as a 'reference' to the material you are mixing. This can help you identify any issues about your listening space and to clarify your ideas about the final sound you are trying to achieve.

▶ SETTING UP YOUR MIXER

Start with the software mixer clearly displayed on screen in front of you, with monitors suitably positioned. Set the software main output level to 0 dB and adjust the control room volume until it's comfortable, making a note of the setting. This ensures a consistent listening volume. If you are going to work systematically through the tracks, pull all the track faders down (no sound) and check that they are all sent to the same output and are free of any effects or other settings left by previous projects or your tracking foldback mix.

INTEGRATING HARDWARE

It is possible to work entirely within the software, in which case your hardware mixer is only acting as a route for the output signal to go to the monitors. However, you may want to use some outboard equipment, maybe for hardware or effects, or perhaps you like the sound of the EQ in your mixer channels. To do this, tracks will have to be individually output to the mixer from an output on your audio interface. As the effect, compression or EQ is applied, the direct output from the mixer channel can then be returned to the audio interface and recorded on a new track, parallel to the original. Mixing can then continue in the software environment. Saving a track that has been processed in some way is known as **printing.**

CONTROL SURFACE

Software mixers can be awkward to use, as sliders and rotary controllers have to be controlled with a mouse. A control surface looks and feels like a real mixer but moves the software controls for you as you move the real ones. It is usually linked to the computer by a MIDI connection and can be set up to correspond with the detailed workings of most well known software. Some smaller keyboards and controllers offer some of the same facilities and can be useful while mixing too.

A TYPICAL MIX

First, think what you are trying to achieve: a noise-free, well-balanced mix of tracks, panned across a stereo field with well-managed dynamics so that you can hear a full range of soft to loud sounds.

Equalisation may improve some of the vocal or instrumental tracks and help them fit into the mix. A little reverb will give a sense of front-to-back spatial awareness and bind everything together into a coherent sound. At the end of the process, the final mix should have a strong level without being so 'hot' (high) that the main output is peaking. If the overall level is too low, trying to bring it up at the mastering or listening stage will amplify background noise too.

Many of these factors will already have been taken care of at the recording stage. Overly complex mixing, with lots of tweaking of EQ, multiple effects and changes is likely to sound unrealistic and messy in the end. A simple, straightforward approach will give good results and you can add more sophistication as you gain experience and learn from others.

> The mix process needs to be cycled through several times, taking plenty of breaks to ensure fresh ears. Each track needs some more individual attention as a rough first mix is built up.

▶ STARTING WITH DRUMS

The overhead microphones record the sound of the whole kit, so one way to get started is to listen to these first. You need a reference level to work to, so you could put the faders at 0 dB in the first instance (the whole level will probably come down later) and adjust the volume on your mixing desk for comfort. They will need to be panned, but if they are fully left and right the drum kit will sound unrealistically wide. Start at the extremes and bring both pan controls in until you have established a suitable stereo field. You may need to adjust the levels so that the sound from both sides of the kit balances.

KICK

Listen to the kick drum on its own. The sound from this track will reinforce the kick in the overhead tracks. Some compression will nearly always help a kick drum sound, evening out the strength of the beats and making it generally sound more 'punchy'. On software mixers, a compressor is chosen from an insert point, which is represented graphically on the channel.

SNARE

The snare drum has a very strong attack. It is important to listen to it to make sure that the sound is appropriate – you may need to make slight EQ adjustments. If you compress it, be aware that too fast an attack time may dull the initial hit, which is the main point of a snare drum in a lot of music. Once you have checked the sounds, pull the snare and kick down and bring the overheads back up. Feed in the snare and kick faders until they reinforce the overhead sound sufficiently – pan the snare until it matches the stereo image of the overheads, slightly to the right.

TOMS

If you have used additional microphones for toms, each needs to be checked on its own. They tend to be played together, so it is important that they balance each other as well as fitting into the overall drum kit sound. A common effect is to hear toms played across the stereo field, so they need to be separated in the panning from left to right, but within the width of the overheads.

> While getting used to the software, choose the default compressor settings and listen to the result. Experiment with different settings and use the Bypass button to hear the sound with or without compression. Push it to extreme levels to hear the sound you don't want and then work back to a sound that you like. A kick drum is usually panned to the centre, a tradition from the days of vinyl when a strong signal to one side could be problematic.

A TYPICAL MIX

▶ MIXING INSTRUMENTS

Bass

The bass nearly always needs some compression. Start gently – compression will help to make the notes sound even and improve the clarity of the sound, but too much will make it lifeless and dull. A little EQ may help, but again, too much can be destructive. Filtering out the very lowest frequencies can clean up the sound, but boost only with caution.

Bass sounds are generally panned in the middle of the field. Try just shifting the bass very slightly apart from the kick drum, so that they are working together rather than against each other.

> Bass sounds need to be set so that the listener is just aware of them, but they don't distract from the melodic interest of the song. Start by finding a level that balances with the drums – important bass lines, riffs and solos can be brought out later in the process.

Piano

As with drum overheads, full left and right panning is likely to sound unrealistic. It is common to have the piano straddling the centre of the stereo field, but it can be shifted to one side providing the separation is maintained between the hands. EQ adjustment may well be needed with piano recordings, perhaps taking a harsh edge off the treble notes or clarifying the bass. As a general rule, slight cutting is likely to be more effective than amplification. If you find you are using a lot of EQ adjustment, maybe the original recording process needs a rethink.

Guitar

If piano and guitar play at different times, panning them on opposite sides can add some interest to the progression of the song. Listen to commercial recordings for ideas on stereo placement – a song with more than one guitar track is likely to keep them clearly separated. The opening balance depends on whether the guitar is playing a solo or accompanying. While building the rough mix, it needs to be balanced so that it is clearly audible along with bass and drums.

Vocals

In the majority of multi-track recordings, the vocal line is the centre of attention for most of the project. It needs to sit clearly in the front of the mix while at the same time blending with the overall sound. It is common practice to centre a single, main vocal track. If there is more than one lead and/or backing vocals, they need to be panned appropriately across the stereo field.

Compression is usually essential, especially for a singer with a wide dynamic range that may dramatically peak or drop to a whisper. Listen to the singer alone – if it is well recorded in the first place, little or no EQ should be necessary. Some can be helpful with a harsh tone, or sibilant ('s') sounds and this will be in the higher frequency bands, away from the main range of the voice.

GROUPS, INSERTS AND SENDS

▶ GROUP TRACKS

Software mixing offers facilities only available on the largest of hardware console mixers. The ability to route any combination of tracks to a group track is one of them. In the sample mix so far, there are four drum tracks. If, having set up the individual drum levels and panning, you need to bring them up or down, then each fader has to be moved while keeping the balance correct between them all. By routing the four tracks to one stereo group track, the drums can all be adjusted at once (see illustration *below*).

▶ INSERTS

Instead of a socket to take the signal out, a software insert point is a graphic button with the same purpose – to interrupt the signal path and process the entire signal on a track. Clicking on an insert button will bring up a menu from which a choice of effects and processors is available. For each track it is possible to add a new compressor and a number of effects. The only limitation on this is the ability of your computer to process all this information. When using a hardware mixer it would be unusual to add an effect such as reverb at an insert point. In a software mixing environment, this is more common when the effect is only needed for one track, with the wet/dry mix being controlled in the effect window. If using more than one insert on a track, compress first, as EQ and effects may affect the operation of the compressor when applied in advance.

▶ SENDS

The more common method of sending an effect to an auxiliary bus and then returning it to the mix is also possible from a software mixer track. Clicking on a send button will offer a menu of auxiliary tracks to send part or all of the signal to using a mouse-controlled fader. The effect is then applied to the auxiliary track then returned to the main mix.

1 Some signal is sent to the Aux 1 track from a send, controlled by the rotary fader.

2 Aux 1 has reverb applied to it as an Insert and is fed back to the mix via the track fader.

3 Compression is applied as an insert. Clicking on it will bring up the compressor window.

4 Each drum track has Group 1 as its output.

5 Group 1 controls the level of all the drums from its one fader, preserving panning and balance.

6 Tracks, group and auxiliary are all mixed to the final stereo output.

SOFTWARE MIXER

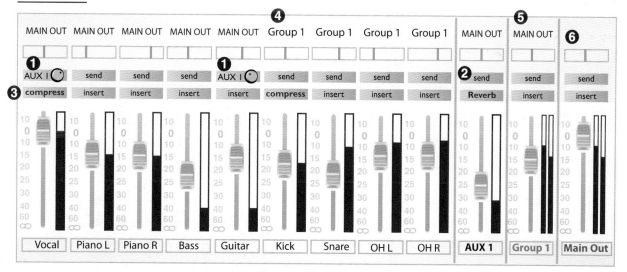

▶CYCLING THROUGH

Having created a rough mix, go through it again paying attention to the overall sound rather than the individual tracks. Play it back, checking that the stereo field works well, and that the instruments are suitably separated without a 'hole in the middle' or other obvious gaps where nothing happens. This will also give you a feel for roughly where the levels should be, particularly how strong the vocal line is in relation to the other tracks.

A general level needs to be found where the vocal is sitting on top of the mix without standing out too much. This needs to be checked at various points in the song, keeping in mind that it won't always be possible and some further adjustment will be needed as the song progresses. If the vocal has to be pushed to a very high level to make it work, bring the other instruments down, or maybe start again with a generally lower level for the accompaniment.

▶EFFECTS

Reverb is the universal effect used to bind a mix together. The more reverberation applied to a sound, the more distant it seems. Vocals need some reverb to help blend them with the other tracks. However, too much reverb will make vocals go backwards in the mix. Using a 'send' means that more than one instrument can use exactly the same effect, keeping a consistent sound.

Software effects units have a range of presets, ready with standard reverb settings, some of which are based on the plate and room reverbs of previous eras – once selected, these settings can be adjusted.

Having chosen a suitable reverb on the auxiliary channel, each track can send its own level of signal to it. Drum overheads, piano and guitar may benefit from a little, especially if recorded in a very dry space but the amount of effect will need to be balanced between the tracks so that the vocal sound is suitably prominent. The effect should be subtle – if delays and echoes are clearly audible there is probably too much. As with many other processes, pushing the settings too far and then working back can be helpful.

▶TRACK AUTOMATION

Now that you have created a basic mix, the fine-tuning can begin. If you are using a control surface, the software can save the movements you make with the faders. If not, levels are usually adjusted by clicking and dragging on an automation track, parallel to the audio track, or by moving the software faders with the mouse. The tracks 'read' (play back) or 'write' (save) the automation data and need to be set to do so. Remember to turn off the write facility when you have finished!

Before software mixing was available it was necessary to 'ride the faders', bringing track levels up and down as the song played through. For example, a guitar might initially play an accompanying role, before playing a solo which would need to be made more prominent. Some hardware mixers have motorised faders that remember the fader movements, and a similar option is now available in most music software.

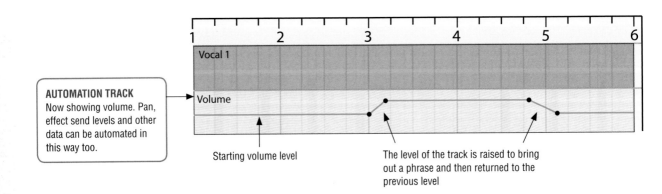

AUTOMATION TRACK
Now showing volume. Pan, effect send levels and other data can be automated in this way too.

Starting volume level

The level of the track is raised to bring out a phrase and then returned to the previous level

POLISHING

Getting a mix to a point where you are satisfied with it involves a lot of listening and fine adjustment. It is important to keep taking breaks and coming back to the mix – long sessions are often wasted time, as after a while your perception of the sound becomes fatigued and needs to be refreshed. During the mixing process, you will need to listen to tracks individually and together and keep switching between the two. Compression, EQ and effects are applied to individual sounds but the final adjustments need to be made while listening to them in the context of the whole mix.

From time to time, change the volume at which you are listening to the mix. Our hearing is not evenly responsive to all frequencies at different volumes. Listening at a lower or higher level will bring your attention to some aspects of the mix you had not noticed before. Another well-known trick is to listen from just outside a doorway when you think you are close to finishing:

- Does the vocal still sit well in the track?
- How is the balance of the bass?

Automation offers the opportunity to make very fine adjustments. This can be used throughout the process, or you may prefer to find a basic level first to which automation can be added later. Everyone develops their own style and mixing process after a while. Previewing a mix on different monitors and headphones is essential – if it is to be distributed then it needs to sound good on a variety of equipment.

▶ PRESETS

Most software has buttons to push for effects and processing, often labelled something like 'female vocal EQ' or 'rock band bass'. These can be useful, but can also sometimes create more problems than they solve. Often, a preset will not just introduce some EQ, as it says on the label, but a variety of other processes as well which you won't be aware of until you start exploring. Clicking a preset on several different tracks can result in a host of effects being applied which may not sit well together in your mix. If you like a preset, look at the settings it introduces and try bypassing some of them to find out what actually makes the difference that you like.

▶ SAVING AND ARCHIVING

As you go on to master a track, it is essential to make sure that the whole project is safely saved. A backup needs to be kept so that you can go back to your original tracks if something goes wrong later on or files are lost. You may decide to revisit a project at some point and maybe create a remix.

Some software has the facility to repackage a project – saving it to a new folder and transferring all the associated audio files while ignoring all the unused ones. This can save storage space, prevent error messages (such as the software trying to find a file that you don't need) and help you to to work in a tidy, disciplined way.

When you are satisfied with your mix, you have a complex project with multiple files that can only be opened by someone with the same software package. For distribution, it needs to be one stereo file that is likely to sound good on a variety of equipment. There are two basic methods for creating a final stereo file:

- Record the main mix output to a new stereo track, using a computer or a stand-alone recorder
- Export ('bounce') the tracks to a new stereo file from within your mixing software.

Recording in real time is essential if you want to include any outboard effects connected to your hardware mixer at the same time. Otherwise a digital export (bounce) is the most straightforward option and avoids more conversion between digital and analog. Having created the file, you need to put it onto a medium for distribution, which could be a CD, MiniDisc, tape, personal music player or server for access across a network or the internet.

Mastering is the process of finalising the product from a mix. This can range from simply burning to CD to a complex process that polishes and refines the mix still further, maximising loudness, adjusting EQ and compression and dazzling the listener with the commercial sparkle of the sound. Specialist mastering studios use dedicated software and hardware to process mixdowns, taking into account the market they are aiming for and the equipment on which the music will be played.

This section will explain how to export a stereo master file, polish and refine tracks, and tips for distributing your music.

▶ EXPORTING A STEREO MASTER FILE

There are some basic mastering processes which will benefit any mix made in a project studio (i.e., not in a commercial environment). Many software packages have built-in tools for mastering. To use these, it is best to export a stereo file first and work on it as a separate project. Alternatively, open it in an audio editor or dedicated mastering software.

All digital recordings have a sample rate and resolution (bit depth). Audio software can work at a higher resolution than the standard CD rate of 44,100 Hz (44.1 kHz) and 16 bit. Resolutions of 24 bit or 32 bit and sample rates of 48 kHz or even 96 kHz are possible. If you know you will be mastering from within the same software, leave any change of rate/resolution until the very end (when making the CD, MP3 or other product), continuing to work at the higher settings during any treatment of the master track. If exporting to other software for mastering, it is again best to export using the existing settings and to leave the other program to make changes at the end of the process.

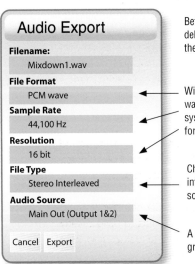

Before making a master track, double-check your mix to make sure that any unused tracks are muted or deleted and that parts are selected or locators placed around the music as necessary. In your software there will be a menu or button that brings up the export dialogue (as shown *left*).

Within this, you will need to choose the bit depth and sample rate as well as the file format. Uncompressed wave files (.WAV) are a standard, cross-platform format. AIFF files are commonly used on Macintosh systems. Windows media audio (.WMA), MP3 and other compressed-distribution formats are not suitable for the mastering process if more editing is needed after the mastering stage.

Check that you have selected a stereo-interleaved track for export. This is a single file that contains the information for both stereo channels. The alternative is 'split' channels, only necessary for import into some high-end software.

A digital export or bounce is taken from a specific output, so it is essential to ensure that any tracks, groups or buses are routed correctly before starting the export.

TIDYING UP

After exporting your stereo master file there is still some tidying up to be done. The first and most obvious step is to 'top and tail' the track, removing any noise or long silences at the beginning and end – but remember to leave room for the sound to fully die away (the reverb 'tail'). A fade in or out may be appropriate, which is easy to add when using software by selecting a section and processing it.

▶ FINAL LEVEL

Check the average level of a stereo track. It needs to be high enough for comfortable listening, especially if it is part of an album or playlist. A very low level means that the player has to be turned up high. As ever, this probably means more noise and a poor listening experience. Large changes in levels between tracks are also unwelcome.

▶ COMPRESSION

In commercial music, this is an important part of the mastering process. In the project studio (non-commercial recording) it needs to be approached with caution. Compressing a whole mix very lightly can enhance the sound, but to be really effective it needs to be done with a multi-band compressor. This allows different settings and responses in various frequency bands, avoiding obvious problems such as a kick drum continuously triggering the compression of a whole mix. A lot of experience and understanding is needed to do this well.

> Since music production became mainly digital, commercial tracks have become ever 'louder', heavily compressed with less and less dynamic range. There are arguments for and against this trend – although heavily compressed audio can sound better on cheaper equipment and over the radio, dynamics are an important part of music and this kind of processing does not suit every style.

▶ NORMALISATION

It is common (but not essential) to normalise tracks as the final process before distribution. Normalisation increases or decreases the overall volume of a track so that the loudest points match a certain volume – often 0 dB, the highest volume that will not distort. Unlike compression, normalisation affects every part of a track equally, so that the original dynamic contrasts are retained.

Normalisation to 0 dB will bring only the peaks of a track up to their maximum possible volume. If it is already at a consistently strong level or has even a few high peaks, this will not make a great deal of difference to the track as a whole. For a track with a low level, full normalisation runs the risk of bringing to the fore all the background noise which could not be heard before.

Normalising can be set to a maximum value below 0 dB, such as -3 dB or -6 dB, which can help to rescue a low-level track without too much extra noise. Alternatively, high peaks in a track can be adjusted by highlighting them and reducing their gain. This will increase the amount by which the average track level is raised during normalisation.

A (short) stereo file exported from a mix

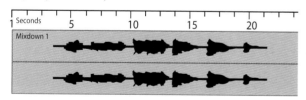

Silence has been removed at the beginning and the enlarged wave form graphic shows that the track has been normalised

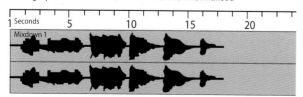

The final level of a master track is dependent on the overall levels in the mix, and the level at which it was exported. If a lot of adjustment is needed, it may be better to revisit the mixing stage.

Audio software usually exports from a specified output and the settings for this will be reflected in the file produced for mastering.

To make a satisfactory CD or other finished product, the final track needs to have a fairly high average level and to be as free from unwanted noise as possible.

CHECKING

You may already have listened to your mix on a variety of speakers and headphones. Before distributing your work to others, submitting it at the end of a course or releasing it on CD, it is essential to take this testing process another step further. A simple way of checking a master track is to burn it on to CD from your computer (see *opposite*) and listen to it on everything you can. An old 'boombox', a computer with speakers, a car stereo system, on a home stereo with good-quality amplifer and speakers and anything else you can find.

- Is the vocal still sitting well in the mix (not lost and not sounding like karaoke)?
- Is there too much or too little bass?
- Do the various instrumental solos achieve the required prominence?
- How does the frequency range sound – is it muddy or too bright?

If it is going to be played on the radio, try a mono mix and feed it to one small speaker.

Listening away from your mixing environment is the important factor. If the track disappoints in the outside world, either the mastering process needs adjusting or, more likely, you need to go back to your mix and make some changes. The level of bass is often deceptive when mixing and the amount of reverb on vocals needs careful adjustment, as do the volume levels of the tracks. Checking a mix away from the workspace will help you adjust the environment you work in – perhaps leading to changes in the acoustic treatment of the room, monitor positioning and so on.

▶ CONVERSION

When preparing your master track for burning to CD, sample rates and bit depth may need to be adjusted. If you are working at a higher resolution such as 24 bit, then a process known as **dithering** needs to be applied as a CD-ready file is created. Without this, some of the digital data is lost as the file is reduced to 16 bit. How dithering is brought into the process varies between different software packages (sometimes it is automatic during conversion). Sample rate conversion and dithering may be available from a DSP (digital sound processing) menu or as a plugin. In some software, dithering is added from an insert point in the master output track and definitely needs to be the last process applied before the file is saved.

If a master track is to be recorded directly to an analog medium such as tape, the quality of the audio output and the equipment handling it is important. If you wish to record to vinyl, then a different mastering process is needed, applying the RIAA EQ curve which helps the creation of a manageable groove in the disc. This is available in some software but is a specialised area of knowledge and experience. The best course here is probably to send your unchanged master track to a specialist vinyl mastering company.

WHY WORK AT DIFFERENT SAMPLE RATES OR BIT DEPTHS?

A higher bit depth stores more information about each sample of sound. This translates into a wider dynamic range and more headroom, so there is less chance of peaking and distortion during recording. The increased bit depth also reduces the effects of the continual mathematical manipulation of the audio while it is in the digital domain.

Higher sample rates are thought by some to offer higher-quality audio, although this is a hot topic of debate. For most of us, 24- or 32-bit resolution will offer some advantages and sample rates of 88.2 and 96 kHz are widely used in recording software and audio interfaces too. Lower sample rates are sometimes used to reduce file sizes and speed up downloads for audio on the internet, but the loss of quality is always apparent.

At the end of the process a CD will need to be 16 bit, 44,100 Hz and this is a perfectly acceptable format to work at throughout a project too.

DISTRIBUTION

▶CD BURNING

It is now very easy to make a CD quickly using computer software – just create a playlist and click the burn button. If you want to work with digital audio to the highest possible quality, though, a little more care needs to be taken.

The main consideration is the **write speed** – the amount of data that is transferred to the CD per second. This transfer speed is labelled as 1x, 4x, 8x and so on (up to ever higher speeds) and refers to a multiple of the playing time of the track. So, a 1x burn speed for a four minute song would take around four minutes and 4x would take one minute. The higher the speed, the more possibility there is of digital errors being introduced. So for the best quality of recording, stick to low speeds, no more than 4x. Alternatively, recordings can be made in real time to a stand-alone CD recorder. The digital output from an audio interface can be directly connected to one of these and, slow though it is, a high-quality disc will be the result.

The quality of CD-burning media varies greatly. In some software, detailed settings are available for the creation of CD tracks, including the red book specification. This lists detailed criteria which must be followed for a commercially mastered CD, and it is essential to work to this standard if you are preparing a master CD for duplication. For a professional result, consideration needs to be given to the relative levels of the tracks, gaps between them and extras such as CD text which will display on players – all part of the final mastering process. Think of the listening experience – long or uneven gaps between tracks and sudden changes of level need to be avoided.

> **TIP**
> For best results, use branded discs intended for audio recording.

▶DIGITAL DISTRIBUTION

Instead of saving your final master file in a CD-ready format, you can simply distribute it for others to listen to on computers or personal music players. The two main issues here are:

- File size
- Audio quality.

CD-quality audio uses about 10 MB of storage per minute of stereo music. For use on personal players and over the internet, this file size needs to be reduced.

By manipulating the digital data, audio files can be '**compressed**' – this has nothing to do with audio compression but simply means making the file smaller. The most commonly used compression format is MP3. There are many varieties of MP3, the most common difference between them being the bit rate – the amount of information that is processed from the file per second. The most common bit rate is 128 kilobits per second, although 192 kbits/s is also quite widely used, with a noticeably better quality. Higher rates are available to a maximum of 320 kbits/s. For comparison, the bit rate of CD playback is 1,411.2 kbits/s.

Most audio software offers the option to export/save as MP3, MP4 and other compressed formats. Convenient though they are, compressed files give lower sound quality, losing both dynamic and frequency range. The final decision about format and settings is a balance between quality and the intended use of the material. If supplying audio tracks for video, you need to find out which format is required. Some video editing programs will only use certain file types, and most of them will compress the audio as they are finalised, so it may be best to supply the highest quality audio file that you can before it is processed further.

> **TIP**
> MP3 and some other distribution formats allow you to add information to 'tags', also called metadata. This can include the title, artist and album and is very useful for archiving and searching.

TEST YOURSELF

▶RECORDING

The production of music is often seen as a complicated and mysterious art, open only to highly trained wizards of the studio.

In fact, it is a straightforward process in which a little common sense is valuable. One of the most important ingredients of success is to keep in mind what you are trying to achieve. For almost every recording this includes avoiding unwanted noise and capturing sound at a good level.

Keep things simple – don't keep adding processes and effects just because you can. There are no hard and fast rules about the capture of sound – if what you are doing sounds right to you, then it is right for your project, however you have achieved it.

A step-by-step approach is also good practice. Don't try to do too much at once and take plenty of breaks when mixing and mastering.

Always remember that you are recording sound – the recording process is not an end in itself. If the sound you are recording is under-rehearsed, out of tune or of a poor quality, then stop and put that right before continuing!

▶TEST YOURSELF

01 What is a potential problem when using 'open' headphones during recording?

02 Suggest two ways of avoiding unwanted noise during recording:

03 From where is it most important to cut sound reflections while recording a singer?

04 What is the digital process of raising a track to its highest possible level called?

05 Which parts of a room should you avoid when positioning monitors for mixing?

06 Which process needs to be applied when the bit depth of a sound file is reduced?

▶ **TRY THIS**

☐ **Do some test recordings** before launching into significant projects. Experiment with microphone choice and placement and all the other stages in the process of recording.

☐ **Get together with some friends** to record a simple song that is easy to play so that you can concentrate on the technology.

☐ **Recording together as a band** to make a guide track will make an interesting experiment. See how much you can separate the sounds of the instruments to give you more control over the mix. It may prove quite a challenge to hear the vocal line!

☐ **Record a piano** with two close microphones. Keep moving them to find the best possible positions.

☐ **Find someone who can play an instrument** such as double bass, violin, saxophone or trumpet. Place a series of microphones around the instrument and record them all on separate tracks. You can then compare the quality of sound capture from different positions.

☐ **Record a drum kit** with just a pair of overhead microphones. Can you position them to capture a realistic sound from the entire kit?

☐ **Set up a microphone to record a guitar amplifier**. Experiment with the positioning, and try mixing the microphone signal with a direct line from the guitar. You may also like to try having another microphone further back in the room.

☐ You need to set up a **foldback system** before you can record successfully. If you are using an existing studio setup, make sure you know how to feed the signals through to multiple performers.

☐ **Create a test mix** once you have recorded a simple song. This will not only improve your mixing skills, but will let you test the accuracy of your listening space. Compare the result on a variety of playback equipment. If you are aiming to release recordings for distribution, it is obviously important to experiment to achieve a suitable level of quality. For exam work it is essential that the work you submit is not your first ever attempt at mixing and mastering!

CHAPTER 10
SEQUENCING

PERFORMANCE AND REALISATION

A sequencer creates a graphical representation of musical data, with coloured tracks and parts, mixers and faders. It offers the choice of recording audio or MIDI data to be played back by real or virtual instruments. This chapter will look at how to set up and start working on a basic sequencing project, particularly a MIDI sequenced performance (or realisation).

Most commercial music now includes some MIDI tracks. A MIDI track can be a useful addition to a multi-track recording, perhaps supplying drum sounds, an extra melodic line or the sound of an instrument that is not readily available live. In contrast, a project with mostly MIDI tracks can be enhanced by live sounds, such as vocals or instruments.

> Advertising, film and multimedia music depend heavily on MIDI projects. A film soundtrack, for example, can be created entirely in this way. It may then be included as it is, or be used to try out the musical ideas before making a score and booking expensive recording sessions.

▶ WHERE DOES THE SOUND COME FROM?

MIDI tracks only store data – commands specifying which sounds should be played and how they should be shaped. Every track has to connect to an instrument. With the sophisticated software we have now, it is easy to create tracks and just choose a 'software instrument' without realising that it is controlled by MIDI data. Before embarking on a MIDI project, you need to give some thought to this – will you be using external keyboards or sound modules, built-in sounds in your software or extra software instruments? Huge collections of sampled sounds are now available that can be played from MIDI tracks. These include sounds of real pianos, instruments and voices and can take up many gigabytes of storage space.

▶ GETTING STARTED

As with audio recording, you need to create a new project that is saved in its own folder. It is worth having a look at the templates in your software – there may be one called something like '16 Track MIDI Sequence' which could save you some setting-up time. In some sequencers, different kinds of MIDI tracks will be available for using built-in software instruments or external instruments. There are three main ways of setting up instruments:

1. Creating an instrument track in your software.
2. Creating a MIDI track output to a channel of an external hardware instrument.
3. Creating a MIDI track output to (a channel of) a software instrument **plugin**.

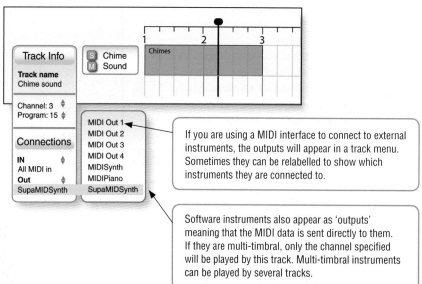

If you are using a MIDI interface to connect to external instruments, the outputs will appear in a track menu. Sometimes they can be relabelled to show which instruments they are connected to.

Software instruments also appear as 'outputs' meaning that the MIDI data is sent directly to them. If they are multi-timbral, only the channel specified will be played by this track. Multi-timbral instruments can be played by several tracks.

A software instrument track will create an 'instance' of an instrument, using one sound which you can select from a menu.

Other virtual instruments exist as plugins. These can be accessed via their MIDI channels in the same way as a hardware instrument. This means several tracks can share an instrument, saving processing power.

Instruments often have a visual interface that includes faders and controls to adjust all of their parameters including the choice of timbre for each channel.

MIDI projects fall into three main categories:

- **Performance (realisation):** performing using MIDI instruments. For example, making a backing track or covering an existing song.
- **Arranging:** a freer version of a piece. This can range from a few small changes (such as instrumentation) to a creative reworking that is only loosely connected to the stimulus material.
- **Composition:** using music software to create a new musical work.

Another term you may come across is **transcription**. This is a version that keeps as close to the original as possible.

Note: arranging and composition are covered in more detail in **Chapter 11**.

When setting up a sequencing project, the first task is to create the required number of tracks and make sure that each one is labelled with the name of the sound (trumpet, piano and so on) that you want to hear. Choosing instruments can be a time-consuming business. To get the project up and running, find a sound close to what you want from a standard instrument and press on. When all the notes are entered and edited, you can go back and change the instrument and timbre on each track to find that perfect sound.

Next, set the opening tempo and time signature. In most software this is done in the transport bar, but there may be a separate tempo track or editor. This will enable you to change the tempo and time signature as the piece progresses.

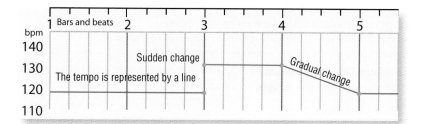

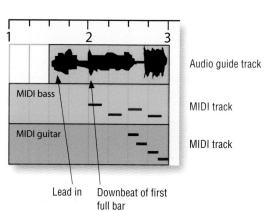

Lead in   Downbeat of first full bar

▶ GUIDE TRACK

If working from a recording to make a cover or backing track, import an audio file into its own track as a guide. You can play or mute the track as you work out the notes. If you can drag it so that the first beat of the first full bar is on a barline, then you should be able to adjust the tempo to fit (listen to the metronome click). However, it may take a number of small changes to get it exactly right.

> **TIP**
> If you have a lot of tracks, create a 'folder' track. You can drag other tracks into this to clear your view of the screen. They continue to play and can be brought out whenever needed.

▶ PLAYING

Whatever kind of project you are working on, the most expressive and musical result is likely to come from playing the notes in using the MIDI keyboard. If you don't play the keyboard already, MIDI sequencing can be an opportunity to develop skills in this area. Work in very small sections and do some simple note recognition and fluency exercises. If you are working from a CD or audio track, just keep repeating a bar or two over and over. You will soon be able to reproduce the small differences that give the music its character.

▶ STEP TIME

An alternative to playing, step time lets you choose a note length and then press the note you want on your keyboard. Every time you play a note, it will be entered on the next beat or division, according to the length you have chosen. If you keep one hand on the mouse to change note length and one on the keyboard for pitches, this will become a fluent way of working.

▶ DRAWING

Notes can be inserted by clicking or dragging on the graphic editor using the mouse. Again, the note length can be set before you click – usually the velocity too, so a two-handed technique can be useful.

▶ WHICH PART TO ENTER FIRST

If transcribing by ear, start with the easiest and most obvious parts. These are likely to be the drums or perhaps a repetitive riff or chord pattern that runs through the piece. If the drums are complex, lay down a simple version first, just to give you a rhythmic base to work with. If it is easy to play the melody line, put that in too – it could just be a guide the first time you play it, and can always be recorded again more accurately at the end. Once you have some easy sections recorded, you can fill in the gaps and work out any tricky parts.

> **TIP**
> When transcribing by ear, use EQ to make the part you are working on easier to hear. By roughly filtering high, middle and low frequencies you can make the bass, melody or any other parts stand out.

▶ MIDI DRUMS

Drum sounds are 'mapped' to the notes of a keyboard. General MIDI instruments follow a consistent mapping. For example, you will always hear a high bongo on note 60 (middle C) and a cowbell on note 56. GM also specifies that drum sounds must be on channel 10 of the MIDI instrument. Some software packages have a specific MIDI drum editor which displays the drum sounds on a grid and timeline and enables you to change the mapping of drums to notes. See **Chapter 6** for more on GM instruments.

When transcribing drum parts, listen for patterns (which may only be a few bars long). You can save a lot of work and time by repeating drum patterns rather than entering every note of the piece. If you do this, make sure the drums do not sound too mechanical by editing the velocity and note lengths within the pattern. If the pattern is repeated many times through the piece, make a couple of slightly different versions of it and mix them up, changing the emphasis on some notes very slightly. You may end up with a structure like that below:

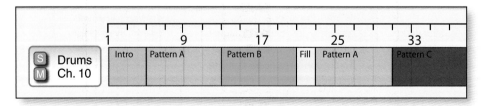

EDITING

▶ GRAPHICS

A graphic editor is a universal feature of MIDI sequencing software. Within it you can see immediately how accurately you have played notes to the beat and can quickly and easily make adjustments. Graphic editors show a keyboard running vertically to indicate which note is being played and a rhythm grid running horizontally into which the notes are fitted. To make the best use of this, it is important to understand the American system of note names:

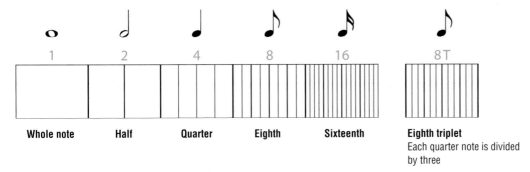

Whole note	Half	Quarter	Eighth	Sixteenth	Eighth triplet

Eighth triplet: Each quarter note is divided by three

The note lengths have a simple relationship, dividing by two at each step. A triplet note is a third of the length of the value above it, represented by a T after the number. For more on graphic editors go to **Chapter 7**.

▶ QUANTISATION

In many sequencers, the number of dividing lines in the grid will change as you adjust the quantise value from a menu. This is especially helpful when entering triplets – choosing a value of 8T, for example, will create a grid where there will be groups of three divisions per beat and the notes can be 'snapped' to them.

The action of quantisation pulls notes automatically towards a rhythmic division. Full quantisation snaps every note to the grid, partial quantisation moves the notes some way towards it and 'groove' quantisation fits the notes to a pre-existing rhythmic pattern (such as a jazz drum groove, for example).

BEFORE QUANTISATION

AFTER QUANTISATION

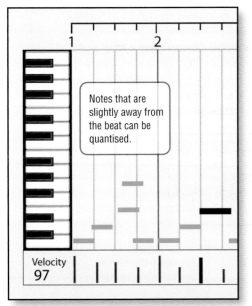

Notes that are slightly away from the beat can be quantised.

Velocity
97

Q

1
2
4
8
16
8T
16T

Quantise menu, set to 1/4 note divisions

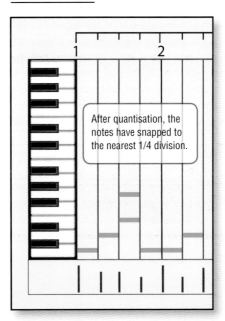

After quantisation, the notes have snapped to the nearest 1/4 division.

Adjusting the length and velocity of notes makes a big difference to the final sound. Notes that are all the same length or velocity will sound very mechanical. To make an effective sequence, it is necessary to go through every part and edit most of the notes. A legato (smooth) effect will be created by full length notes. While this effect is necessary sometimes, it will not sound realistic all the time. Phrasing is created by a combination of gaps between notes and the emphasis placed on them. In a standard $\frac{4}{4}$ bar, for example more emphasis is usually placed on the first and third beats of the bar. This is edited by changing the velocity values, which is usually possible graphically.

GRAPHIC EDITOR WINDOW

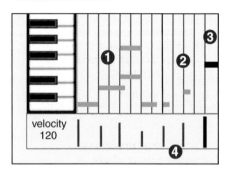

1 Legato and overlapping notes.

2 Short (staccato) notes.

3 Selected note – its velocity value is displayed.

4 Careful velocity editing adds musical shape to the melody.

It's important to keep listening back while editing. For shorter or staccato notes, for example, gaps cannot be judged just by looking at the graphics.

> **TIP**
> Quantisation can be a tempting shortcut here, but should be used with caution. It can make the piece sound robotic if universally applied. One approach is to quantise drum parts and perhaps some of the accompaniment but to leave the melody line as natural as possible, using only manual shaping.

▶ **CONTROLLERS**

Once a fair amount of the note entry has been completed, it's a good idea to set up a stereo field. Some separation of instrumental sounds makes the editing easier. Pan values can be controlled graphically, although it's unlikely you will want to change them during a piece except as a special effect, so they are probably best entered at the beginning of the piece using the list editor. Review this at the end of the project – draw a diagram of the instruments on stage from left to right and work out the pan values: fully left = 0, centre = 64, fully right = 127.

A MIDI project has to be balanced in the same way as a multi-track recording, so volumes need to be set at the beginning for each track and may need to be automated as the piece runs through. Again, this can often be drawn into the graphic editor. As you draw, controller messages are entered and saved. You can see these by opening a list or event editor.

Some MIDI sequencers allow you to control the tracks using a MIDI mixer, with faders and pan controls, or track automation as on audio tracks. This is fine for quick work or if you are going to be using the same software through all stages of a project, but you need to keep in mind that this MIDI data may not all be retained as events or commands. For permanent, foolproof changes you need to make sure that MIDI data is being entered in the file.

Every track needs a volume to start with to set up an opening balance. One way to do this is to set them all to the same value and then change them (mainly downwards) one by one to get to the right blend. Then work through the project making adjustments as you go. Expression (controller 11) is intended to give fine control over the dynamics of a track, working within the level of the main volume (controller 7).

> **TIP**
> See page 64 for more on how controller messages work.

SETTING-UP CONTROLLERS

When a MIDI performance begins, it is very important that all the sounds, volume, pan and other controllers are properly set up. A live performance could be ruined by an error and much frustration can be caused when recording if tracks do not play back as they should. At the end of a piece, for example, some controllers may have been faded to zero – when you start again, those values may still affect playback.

To avoid this, set up a bar for each track at the beginning of a piece, with the musical events beginning a little later. A program change will set the timbre for the track along with volume and pan controllers. Other messages can reset the sequencer so that you will always have a clean start to your performance.

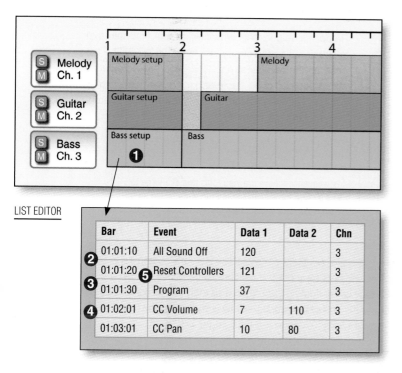

LIST EDITOR

Bar	Event	Data 1	Data 2	Chn
01:01:10	All Sound Off	120		3
01:01:20	Reset Controllers	121		3
01:01:30	Program	37		3
01:02:01	CC Volume	7	110	3
01:03:01	CC Pan	10	80	3

❶ A one-bar-long part contains a series of setting-up commands that can be set or viewed in the list editor.

❷ Controllers stop any instruments playing and reset controller values to default.

❸ A program change specifies which instrumental sound will play.

❹ Opening volume and pan are set.

❺ MIDI timing is in bars, beats and a further subdivision sometimes called ticks. 480 ticks per quarter note is a common setting. These controller messages have been separated slightly within the beat.

> **TIP**
> If you draw in a lot of controller information, the amount of data may affect the performance – this is known as **MIDI choke**.
>
> Some sequencers have a menu command to 'thin out' data, just keeping important steps in such as a change of volume.

► **COLOURED GUIDE**

When setting up a sequence, it is really helpful to know which section you are working on. A spare track with no instrument connected can act as a guide. Create a block for each verse, chorus, bridge or other section and colour-code them. When editing, or copying and pasting, this will help you to navigate the project.

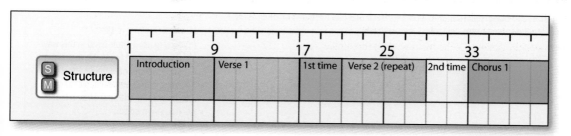

▶ REALISTIC PERFORMANCE

When recording or programming (manually entering data for) a MIDI performance, keep in mind the way instruments actually play, as keyboard input can impose its own style on everything. One example of this is with strummed guitar chords. As a guitar is strummed, the notes are slightly separated – this staggering can go in either direction, depending on whether the guitarist plays an upstroke or downstroke.

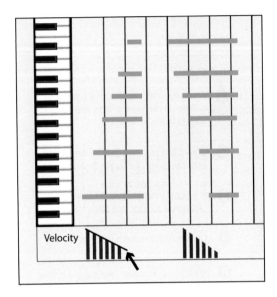

To create a strummed guitar chord, stagger the start of the notes by a very small amount. This can be done freely or by setting a small quantise grid and snapping the notes to it.

Ramp the velocities downwards, as the first note that is struck will be the strongest – and this will still be the case on the reverse strum. Once you have created a chord, you can copy, paste and move the notes to new pitches. For extra realism, make a few slightly different patterns and mix them up.

> Most sequencers have drawing tools that allow you to create a ramp for velocity, fading out volume and so on.

▶ PITCH BEND

Guitars often slide or bend notes, and one of the best ways of reproducing this in MIDI is to use the pitch bend wheel on a keyboard. It is difficult to do this live, so record the note first and then add the pitch bend afterwards. The pitch-bend data can be recorded on a separate track, making it much easier to edit and retake.

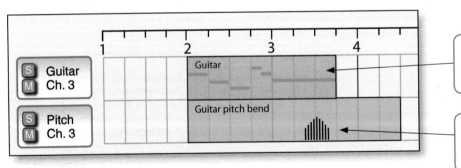

> One long note is entered. It sounds like two notes joined by a bend when played back.

> The pitch bend data is recorded on a parallel track and sent to the same channel.

The notes are recorded first. While playing back, you can practise putting in the pitch bend using the controller wheel. When ready, record it onto a parallel track that has the same channel setting. Any messages sent to the same channel will affect the playback.

> **TIP**
> Having used pitch-bend in this way, it is important to reset it to prevent subsequent notes being affected. Draw a pitch-bend value of zero in the graphic editor or enter it in the list/event editor.

▶ POLISHING

▶ PITCH-BEND WHEEL RANGE

On MIDI keyboards, the controller wheel moves the pitch of a note up or down to a maximum of two semitones by default. However, this can be easily changed by entering a few controller messages. Create a small part in your pitch-bend track, open the list (or event) editor and put in five closely spaced controller messages (CC). Set them up as in this table, and play through them. The next time you play on that channel, the wheel will have a different range.

Bar	Event	Data 1	Data 2	Chn
06:01:10	RPN LSB	100	127	3
06:01:20	RPN MSB	101	127	3
06:01:30	DataEnt	6	12	3
06:01:40	RPN LSB	100	0	3
06:01:50	RPN MSB	101	0	3

The semitone range is set in Data 2
12 semitones = 1 octave
The maximum setting is 24 semitones, or two octaves up or down.

Registered Parameter Number Least Significant Bit (RPN LSB) and Most Significant Bit (PPN MSB) set up the data entry (it isn't necessary to understand all the details of the MIDI protocol to use it).

This technique can be used to make wide, sweeping glissandi, fall-offs and other musical effects. After the notes using it, add another section using the same five controller messages resetting the wheel (Data 1 = 6, Data 2 = 2) to default.

▶ MODULATION

The other wheel on a MIDI keyboard is for modulation. This rapidly varies the frequency of a note giving the effect of vibrato. Modulation (controller 1) is another controller that is best left until after notes have been entered. To make the most effective use of it, apply it sparingly, keeping in mind the musical effect. Too much modulation is definitely not a good thing! Singers and instrumentalists often introduce vibrato towards the end of a long note, sometimes increasing or decreasing the amount as it goes on. It is unusual and unlikely to be desirable to have vibrato or modulation on short notes or all notes. Practise using the modulation wheel as you play back a track and record it when you are ready. Modulation can be edited graphically and in the list editor.

▶ EFFECTS

Some MIDI instruments have built-in effects, such as reverb, which can be applied to their sounds using a continuous controller. This won't work on all instruments, so you need to check the hardware or software settings. CC91 (reverb) is the most common effect to add, and there are a few others that will be useable on some instruments (shown *right*).

Controller no.	Controller	Usual effect
91	Effect depth 1	Reverb
92	Effect depth 2	Tremolo
93	Effect depth 3	Chorus
94	Effect depth 4	Detune
95	Effect depth 5	Phaser

A MIDI sequencer creates an elaborate graphical representation of the data, with coloured tracks and parts, mixers, faders and the appearance of a virtual studio. To play the MIDI music, though, all that is needed is the information about events and controllers, along with suitable instruments. A MIDI file stores just MIDI data in the same way that a plain text file stores only letters and numbers, without all the details added by word processing software. MIDI files can be opened by programs that play them (including most software media players) or imported into other music software to be edited again.

There are two types of MIDI file:

| Type 1 | Preserves the track settings of the MIDI data. Essential for re-importing to another editor or notation program |
| Type 0 | Merges all the data to a single track. Mainly used for simple playback |

When creating a MIDI file, you may need to select parts, add locators on the timeline or specify a range of bars. Check carefully before and after you create the file. Once it is saved, make sure you can import it again and that all the data is there before sending it to someone else.

During the export process, you need to make sure that all the details of the music are captured.

Using a sophisticated sequencer, you can quickly make all kinds of settings such as timbre, pan, volume and delay in the track info (sometimes called inspector) box, as well as in mixers and editing screens. Some of this information is added 'on the fly' (as the track runs) and may not actually be specified as events in the list editor. You may need to go through the piece and enter this data graphically or from the list editor – or sometimes a dialogue box will appear asking if you want to include it:

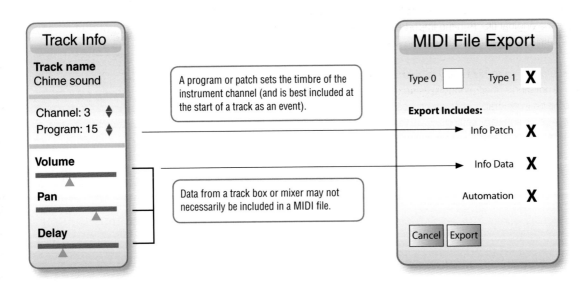

MIDI OUTPUT

▶ DATA TO AUDIO

When a MIDI sequence is finished, it needs to be performed or recorded. For live events, computer-driven MIDI tracks can be performed along with audio tracks and live performance through the stage mixing desk. If a complete MIDI sequence is to be recorded, its instrumental outputs need to be recorded as audio tracks. If this involves any external hardware instruments, it will have to be done by playing back in real time and recording the audio outputs of the instruments. Software instruments can be recorded in the same way, but can also be 'bounced' or exported to make a mixdown stereo file in most software. Some applications will also allow internal routing, so that the output of the MIDI instrument can go to an audio track for recording without leaving the software.

▶ INTEGRATED TRACKS

When a project includes MIDI and audio tracks, a final stereo mixdown has to include the sound of both.

The MIDI and audio tracks need to be mixed together so that the outcome sounds realistic and suitably blended. This can be done using a software mixer that incorporates both the MIDI and audio tracks and it may be possible to process or put effects onto the output bus of the software instruments.

An alternative is to convert the MIDI to audio tracks, either by bouncing them in software or recording them back to audio tracks in the same project. They will need to be panned and balanced again and can have the same effects applied to them as the live tracks that have been recorded.

▶ NOTATION

Most sequencers have some kind of score editor. They vary greatly in quality and ease of use. The score display is a graphic representation of the MIDI data and is not usually suitable for editing or entering notes.

Sequencer scores are often good enough to generate a quick part for someone to play or learn where the appearance is not so important, but rarely good enough to produce a full score.

For a high-quality score, export your sequence as a MIDI file and then import it into a dedicated notation program. There will be import dialogue boxes asking for guidance about the shortest note, triplets, tracks, instruments and other features of the original file. Run the import process several times while changing these settings to get the best possible starting score.

Before exporting, save a separate copy of your sequence and quantise it strictly so that the notation software can easily recognise the note lengths and where they should be in the bar.

> **TIP**
> When recording audio tracks with a MIDI backing, it is best to have full control over the mix, keeping all tracks separately balanced and panned. Recording with a stereo mixdown will sound unrealistic and it will be hard to blend the live tracks in (rather like karaoke).

CHAPTER 11
ARRANGING AND COMPOSING

ARRANGING

▶ WHAT IS ARRANGING?

The expressions 'performance', 'realisation' and 'transcription' are widely used to mean a relatively faithful reproduction of a piece, either by live performers or as a MIDI sequence. Arranging implies something more creative, taking the stimulus material and making a new version of it. For example, in the commercial world this could mean producing several versions of the music for an advertisement, each one based on a different style (rock, classical, jazz) or maybe to suggest different parts of the world. Similar projects are often set as coursework in music technology courses, a good preparation for composition and future professional work.

> **TIP**
> Remember that arranging is primarily a musical task, with technology as a tool to help you.

▶ THINKING ABOUT IT

Although MIDI arranging is a computer-based activity, the first and most important step is to turn away from the computer and have a good think! A successful creative arrangement changes or develops aspects of the original music while keeping the listener aware of what it is based on. Here are some ideas to get you started:

Style	**Think of a style:** reggae, punk, folk, rock, Baroque, techno, ballad, brass band, trad jazz, soul, blues, funk and so on **Work out what characterises your chosen style:** instrumentation, rhythm, riffs, structure, bass lines, harmony, drum patterns and so on
Tempo and time signature	**Dramatically change the tempo:** compare 'Ticket to Ride' by the Beatles and later the Carpenters to hear the difference this can make **Change the time signature:** a square $\frac{4}{4}$ could become a lilting $\frac{6}{8}$, or a waltz could become a march by changing the rhythm, adding or subtracting extra beats **Add an occasional bar with a different time signature:** this can add a quirky highlight to a piece
Instrumentation	**Experiment with unusual instruments:** for example the sitar or accordion **Explore instrumental features:** brass can be open or muted, strings can be bowed or pizzicato (use program changes for different timbres). Woodwind can be really interesting at extremes of high or low pitch (for example a breathy, low flute sound) **Try Solo or Pad (ensemble) timbres:** sometimes a fuller sound will be more suitable
Keys and chords	**Change key:** this helps to maintain interest in longer pieces. It's easy to change to or from major to minor, for example **Change some or all of the underlying chords**
Texture and contrast	**Experiment with texture:** not all of the instruments need to play all the time! Avoid simply putting the melody on one high instrument and working downwards through the other parts. Try swapping the melody between instruments or even put it in the bass. Stop the drums for a while or give them a solo **Vary dynamics:** contrasts in volume are essential to an interesting arrangement

GETTING STARTED

To arrange a piece of music, you need to identify the material you will use as a stimulus. This could be the main melody, the riff that introduces or runs through the piece, the bass line, a rhythmic figure or a chord sequence. You could use all of these or just one, as long as the listener identifies with the original work. You can add extra material of your own or combine themes together.

Try playing the melody first, even if you are not an accomplished keyboard player. It may take practice, but will help stimulate creativity. If you make mistakes (such as getting the rhythm wrong) they may even become the basis for your new ideas!

- Work out the chords, the bass line and any other parts you can pick out on a keyboard (or other instrument that you play) and see how you can develop them
- Just part of a melody can make a good intro – try staggering the start with several instruments playing it in succession
- Vary the rhythm, speed or time of a melody to create a solo
- If you have been given a different style to work to, try modifying the bass of the stimulus to be like the bass of a piece in the other style.

Once you are familiar with the feel of the material, think about structure. Commercial briefs may only be seconds or minutes long, and the structure will be dictated by the underlying content of the video advertisement or other material. Arrangements of whole pieces will need more conventional building blocks such as intro, verse, bridge, chorus and coda.

Sequencing software offers a graphic way to lay out an arrangement. Work out roughly the number of bars that you need and then create a guide track labelled with suggestions for the sections.

Choose your instruments and start to put in ideas at any point in the piece. One way to map out an arrangement is to decide who will have the melody in each section, making sure that there are contrasts and changes of texture.

When you have a coherent structure, with some material for each section, go through the piece and fill in the gaps, adding bass lines, accompaniments, drums as appropriate. Avoid having everyone play at the same time too often – save this for a few important sections.

	1	9	17	25	33
Guide track	Intro / Verse 1	1st / Verse 2	2nd / Chorus 1	Sax solo	
Sax				Melody variation	
Trumpet	Melody				
Guitar	Intro		Melody variation		
Strings		Melody			
Bass					
Drums					

Beginning creative work can be the hardest part, so get started as soon as possible. You may have an idea for a variation of a melody or perhaps a great ending – put that in and it will stimulate more ideas around which you can build.

WHAT IS SAMPLING?

▶ SAMPLED SOUNDS

Sampling means recording an individual sound or section of music. Sounds are sampled for use in instruments, both software and hardware. Drum beats, guitar riffs, vocal sounds, animal noises and all kinds of sounds can be sampled, processed, looped and used in any way you like.

The very earliest samplers stored sounds on short tape loops triggered by keyboards. The most famous of these is probably the Mellotron, one of the key instruments in progressive rock in the 1970s. These were complex and fragile instruments and were replaced by digital samplers from the 1980s onwards.

Digital sampling solved two major issues in sample processing – tempo change and pitch shift. If a tape recording is slowed down the pitch becomes lower, but the speed also becomes slower, giving the zombie or chipmunk (if you speed up) effect. Digital technology can break the link between tempo and pitch.

> **TIP**
> There are two uses of the word 'sampling' in music technology. It can also mean the process of converting an analog audio signal to digital data. One sample is the smallest section of audio that is analysed. See **Chapter 1**.

▶ HOW TO SAMPLE

A lot of sampling is processed using computer software. There are also keyboard workstations with built in samplers and all kinds of hardware sampling devices which will record, manipulate and process sounds. These are used by drummers to trigger samples, by club performers and as part of many artists' studio and composition setup.

Making your own samples is easy. Just record a sound at the best quality you can with some silence either side of it. The minimum of noise is necessary as you will probably need to normalise the recording. There are many handheld digital recorders available now which are ideal for this. To avoid unwanted noise when using one of these, mount it on a stand or put it on a flat surface rather than holding it.

A commonly sampled sound is that of a cymbal:

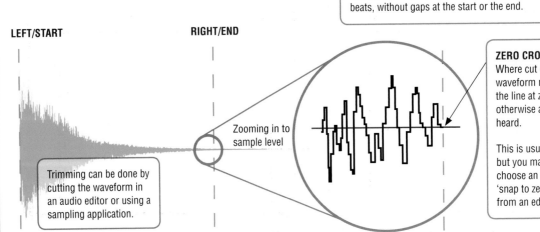

To use the sample, it needs to be trimmed to a length that suits your project, either in seconds or in bars and beats, without gaps at the start or the end.

LEFT/START

RIGHT/END

Zooming in to sample level

ZERO CROSSING
Where cut or joined, the waveform needs to cross the line at zero amplitude, otherwise a click may be heard.

This is usually automated but you may need to choose an option like 'snap to zero crossing' from an editing menu.

Trimming can be done by cutting the waveform in an audio editor or using a sampling application.

USING SAMPLES

Individual samples can be imported to audio tracks and used as part of the music or as special effects.

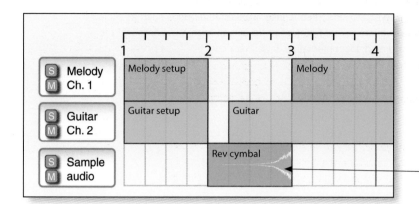

Samples can be processed in many ways, as the sound is stored as digital information.

Reversed samples of percussive instruments such as cymbals and piano notes are popular effects.

This one-bar cymbal sound has been reversed and imported to an audio track, snapping to the barline.

To use sounds in this way, keep the samples in the highest quality format that you can. Wave files of at least 16 bit, 44,100Hz will match the quality of other recorded tracks.

▶ SLICING AND LOOPING

Changing the tempo of a drum beat or guitar riff, or fitting a sound to a beat can be difficult to achieve by adjusting it in an audio editor. Specialist sampling software helps trim, slice and adjust tempo and pitch as well as adding a number of effects. When the sample is exported it can be looped (repeated) to make a full track.

DRUM BEATS IN SAMPLING SOFTWARE

Start and end points are set, and the software has identified the original tempo, but no bar limit has been specified.

A tempo and bar length are set – the slices then move to fit the beats, fixing the timing and the length of the sample.

Pitch can be shifted up and down, changing key for musical sounds.

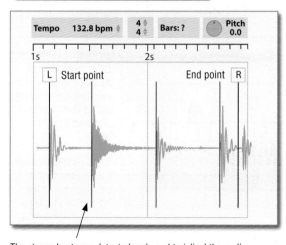

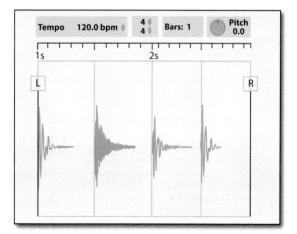

The strong beats are detected and used to 'slice' the audio.

The trimmed sample can now be exported and looped.

The tempo can be changed by moving the separate slices as the beats move closer or further apart. Beyond a certain point, this starts to sound strange.

COMPOSING USING TECHNOLOGY

▶ WHO ARE YOU COMPOSING FOR?

There are two fundamental reasons for composing. One is because you have ideas which you would like to express for your own satisfaction. The other involves creating music for someone else, working to a brief – such as project work for exams. Self-motivated composition gives you complete freedom to do as you wish, but composing to a brief usually means working within certain limits of timing, instrumentation, style and cost.

▶ GETTING STARTED

Before composing a piece, think about what resources are available to you.

You could use:
- Recordings of instruments or singers
- Samples of real-world sounds or tracks
- Pre-recorded loops
- MIDI sequencing
- Keyboards, synthesisers, decks and hardware samplers.

At the end of the process you need to have a finished track for others to use or play, and possibly a musical score or instructions of some kind for performers.

As with sequencing and arranging, an idea of structure is essential when working to a brief. You are unlikely to simply improvise without time or limitation unless you are just exploring artistic ideas on your own.

A sequencing application offers the most efficient way of bringing everything together and putting it into some sort of order. The most obvious benefit of working this way is the use of a timeline. If you are asked to compose music for an advertisement, film or TV show, timing will be very detailed with the brief broken down into sections. Traditionally, composers have used tempo and time signature to synchronise music with other media and in a sequencer this is laid out visually for you:

At 120 bpm there are two beats per second. So in $\frac{4}{4}$ time, one bar is two seconds long. Using this relationship, the sections of a brief can be mapped out with exact timings.

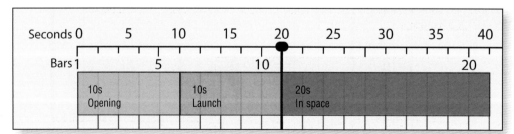

COMPOSING USING TECHNOLOGY

▶ TIME TOOLS

When working to time, look out for helpful features in your software. It may be that you have recorded an idea that is just right for a section, but it is slightly too short. Time stretch or warp tools can drag a part to fit or adjust the tempo of the piece without affecting the pitch. As with sliced samples and pitch shifts, this only works effectively within certain limits. If pushed too far it will begin to sound strange and should only be used for small adjustments.

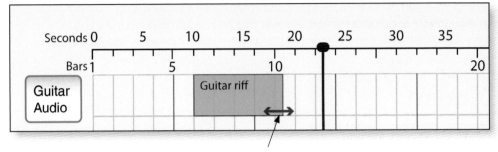

This recording needs to be exactly 10 seconds long. The time stretch tool drags it to length and then adjusts the audio to fit.

▶ WORKING METHODS

Working from a brief may give a time structure, but you still have to think of ideas to fulfil it. Inspiration can come from a melody, chords, a rhythm, a riff or sounds from the world around you. If you have an idea, play it, record it or sequence it to get you started.

Once you have your idea, work out how it can fit into the scheme of your composition. A theme may be needed to unify several sections. If your idea can be varied in some way, it could be the link – can you vary it to suggest different ideas? Maybe change from major to minor, alter the speed or the rhythm.

Motifs are often used to represent characters, locations or objects. A motif can range from a couple of notes to a full orchestration of a melody. Thinking of motifs (melodic, rhythmic or harmonic) is another way of getting a project going.

▶ SEQUENCING AND LOOPING

A sequence including MIDI tracks and audio loops can form the basis of most commercial composition. A rhythmic or chordal basic structure can quickly be constructed by dragging pre-recorded loops onto the timeline. You can improvise over this or add in your riffs, samples, melodies or other ideas to check how they sound. The temporary loops can be deleted as the composition builds.

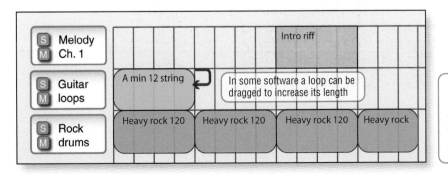

Loops can be a building block of a composition or just act as a temporary scaffolding. They tend to be saved in a variety of tempi and keys.

COMPOSING WITH SAMPLES

Real world sounds can give a composition an extra dimension.

You can record anything, from a hammer hitting some steel to a flower rustling in the breeze. These sounds can then be trimmed, processed and replayed in a multitude of different ways.

Sampled sounds can be used as effects overlaid on a musical 'bed' or they can form part of the music themselves. A melody could be made from animal noises, for example, or a percussion rhythm from a creaking gate. You can create a drum kit by making noises yourself and processing them. This kind of recording and manipulation of sound is a common technique in 'foley' – the noises added onto a film sound track (for example, a monster walking sound made by slurping mouth noises).

ONE BAR OF RHYTHM CONSTRUCTED FROM SAMPLES:

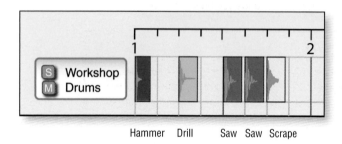

Hammer   Drill   Saw Saw Scrape

▶PROCESSING

Sampled sounds can be processed in many ways.

Extreme settings can produce interesting and useful effects – try severe EQ, filters, over-compression, flange, phasing and other effects to produce something unrecognisable from the original recording.

▶COLLAGE

You don't have to work to a strict timeline or to a brief. Some composers work solely with recorded sound – editing, processing and layering it. Fascinating soundscapes can be produced by recording the spoken word, natural sounds or recordings of sounds that would not normally be audible, such as that made by tiny insects or inside machinery. Your only limitation here is your imagination, as sequencing software offers a canvas on which you can assemble a collage of any sounds you have available together with almost unlimited tools with which to manipulate them.

▶REAL INSTRUMENTS

If your composition is MIDI-based, try adding or substituting a couple of live tracks. A real string section, brass or drums can bring a sequence to life. If you are working with an accomplished performer, play your MIDI composition to them as foldback. Keep recording to new audio tracks as they listen and either play back what they hear or improvise around it. You can then remix the project, blending in the live sounds.

COMPOSING WITH TECHNOLOGY

▶ SAMPLE MAPPING

Some keyboards have built-in sampling facilities which allow you to record a sound, process it and then trigger it from a key or drum pad.

▶ MIDI-CONTROLLED SAMPLING

Hardware samplers will store sounds and map them to keys on a MIDI keyboard. This involves pitch-shifting (transposing) the sounds as they move away from the original frequency.

Once the pitch-shifting has gone beyond a certain point, some realism is lost from the timbre of the recording. To create your own sampled instrument, you need to make recordings of a sound at various pitches, between which the notes are created by pitch shifting. This is known as **multi-sampling**.

Software samplers will also allow connection of a MIDI keyboard to control the sounds. They can be linked to sequencing software and played like any other virtual instrument using the sounds you have created.

MUSIC AND TECHNOLOGY

It is important to keep in mind the distinction between music and sound effects. Unless sampled sounds are used in a musical way they may not be what is wanted by whoever is commissioning your work. This is especially important when producing examination material, and in the commercial world sound effects will be produced by a separate team.

Technology has developed very quickly and we are all offered a bewildering array of sophisticated tools with which to create music. Pre-recorded samples and loops offer the opportunity to create tracks very quickly and it is possible to be very imaginative and creative by using music technology in this way.

To be able to tailor your compositions to suit any project, any knowledge of music that you can aquire will help. Understanding harmony, rhythm and orchestration will enable you to move away from obvious paths that have been trodden many times before. Learning to play any instrument is a good way to increase your understanding of music. Try to find a teacher who is knowledgeable and willing to integrate some theoretical understanding with the development of playing skills.

▶ MUSIC FOR EVERYONE

Recent technology has created music-making opportunities for everyone, whether or not they play an instrument. Playing by ear, scratching with decks, mixing real-world sounds and improvising with electronic instruments all have a part in the rich landscape of modern commercial music and there are plenty of succesful musicians who can't read a note of music. Whatever your interests or skills, music technology can enable you to put your imagination to work!

▶ **SEQUENCING**

The combination of keyboard and timeline in music sequencing programs has largely replaced manuscript paper and pencil in commercial composition.

Sequencing of MIDI and audio has become the framework around which audio projects are built. This working method is mirrored in the world of video editing, where clips are placed on a timeline, edited and processed.

Sequencers now usually have video tracks or windows to allow you to compose to picture. Audio is becoming part of a multimedia workflow with ever-increasing crossover between applications and processes.

Your interest may be in film-making, educational video for the web or composing your own chill-out tracks. With a decent microphone and software, it is possible to produce high-quality audio tracks for all kinds of projects at home.

If you are working to a brief, make sure to stick strictly to the timings. Motifs can be a powerful way of reinforcing the drama of a clip for which you are composing. If several separate sections are requested, try to link them in some way with a common musical idea.

Whichever medium you are writing for – theatre, TV, film, video – get to know something of the specialist working methods and language.

▶ **TEST YOURSELF**

01 What is the difference between a realisation and an arrangement?

02 What does quantisation do?

03 What is the length of this note? ♪

1/2 1/4 1/8 1/16 1/32

04 What is the maximum range of a pitch bend wheel in each direction?

8 semitones 12 semitones 24 semitones

05 Which musical technique is reproduced by Controller 1, Modulation?

Vibrato Tremolo Pizzicato

06 What is the main difference between MIDI files of Type 0 and Type 1?

▶ TRY THIS

☐ **Record the sound** of a finger sliding round the rim of a wine glass.

Change the pitch by altering the amount of water in the glass. Record several pitches of a good length so that you can choose the clearest section of the recordings.

☐ **Transfer the samples** to your computer and trim them to obtain clear sounds of various lengths and pitches.

☐ **Process the samples** in lots of different ways. If you use extreme enough settings, all kinds of sounds will emerge that can be used in your composition.

☐ **Start a new project** with a science fiction theme. It could be a trailer for a film, less than a minute long. Use the samples to make out-of-this-world sounds to go with your sequenced music. With some processing they could be ray guns or spaceship engines.

☐ **Make a completely different piece** starting with the same samples – perhaps dreamy, relaxation music using just the glass sounds, or maybe with some gentle backing.

☐ **Import the sounds** to a software (or hardware) sampler. Can you play them with a keyboard?
The pure tone of a glass could make a sweet melody – maybe a waltz with a MIDI accompaniment.

CHAPTER 12
MUSIC TECHNOLOGY TIPS

STUDIO PRACTICE

▶**BEST PRACTICE IN THE STUDIO**

Whether you are working in a home studio, a school or college or even a state-of-the-art professional studio, there are some common sense routines and courtesies that will make work more efficient. With a little discipline, projects will be of a higher quality, equipment will stay in good condition and everyone will get along!

Label mixer channels by instrument and vocal type
Stick some electrical tape along the bottom edge of the mixer and write on it. Lots of time can be wasted looking for faults while moving the wrong fader!

Set up foldback before performers arrive and test it
Run a CD through the desk for testing, and make sure you have enough headphones and long enough leads.

Make sure you have adequate lighting.
Clip-on stand lights can help with lyrics.

Check all equipment for noise, buzzes, rattles and safety.
Amplifier cabinets, headphones, DI boxes – anything can have loose screws, loose wires or noisy panels.

Put a spare microphone in the live area so you can hear the performers speak to you.
Put it on a channel near your operating position so you can turn it off when not needed.

KEEP EVERYTHING TIDY

Performers who trip over cables won't be able to play for you (and may sue you).
Untidy studio spaces lead to accidents, broken equipment and slower progress!

- **Clear a space for instrument cases:** this helps speed things up when performers arrive, prevent mess and trip hazards
- **Keep drinks, food and clothing away from equipment:** spilt drinks will permanently ruin expensive gear and your project. Carelessly left jackets can get caught in faders or cables and pull equipment off a desk – hang them up out of the way.

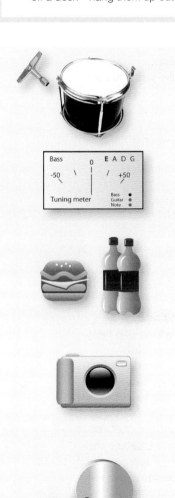

Tune and check drums
Slack drum heads, buzzing snares or rattling stands will bring down the quality of your music making.

Decide on a tuning reference: piano, guitar, electronic tuner or tuning fork? Keep checking before and during every session. Remember that pianos go out of tune over time.

Have some food and drink available for long sessions
Concentration goes when people are hungry or thirsty.
Stop for a break and go to a different space to eat and drink.

Take a photo of your mixing desk and hardware setup
This way, if someone changes anything between sessions you can reset quickly. This is also useful for exams and archives, so you can revisit this work again in the future.

Zero the desk
When you have finished, pull down all faders. Set all pan central. Turn off/neutralise all EQ. Turn down master volume controls. Turn off anything not needed – mix, groups, any other routing and patching. It's a courtesy to other users so they don't waste time setting up or wonder why their mix isn't working. If you know you are coming back soon and want to leave things set up, put a notice on the desk asking others not to change it.

Tell other people what you are doing

Otherwise, they may wander into your session making lots of noise, or ask why you have drawn all the curtains on a summer day?

Leave plenty of time for mixing and mastering

If you have a deadline to meet, get on with the recording and sequencing.

Last minute, hasty mixing and mastering will not produce the best result for a client, an examiner, yourself or your fans.

Plan session times so that you are not rushed

Don't start ten minutes before the school bell goes when the corridors will be full of noisy people.

Put up signs to keep noisy people away

Only use them when you are actually recording, or people will ignore them.

Use a red light

If you don't have one as part of your studio, make your own with a large LED, battery and switch. It helps to create an atmosphere of concentration in a studio situation. But keep in mind that red lights make some performers nervous and sometimes it is best not to use them.

Put one outside the door for unwanted noisy visitors. Only use it when recording, otherwise people will ignore it and come in anyway.

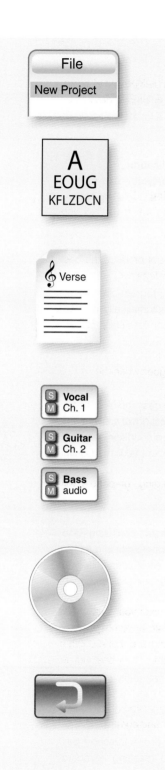

Be ready before performers arrive
They will get bored and won't want to play for you again if you keep them hanging around while you put mics on stands, set up a new project and so on.

Use large type for musical parts and lyrics
Have them ready before you start a session.

Give performers music or a recording of the parts you want them to play well before the recording. It's usually too late, if you want a good outcome, to be learning the music during the session.

Label tracks clearly with the name of the instrument.

Listen to CDs of music that you like in your studio workspace
This will help you set up the listening environment and give you ideas about mixing, balance, effects and everything else concerned with making good recordings.

Use cycle mode for mixing and recording
Set the in and out points and just keep repeating a section – record over it or keep listening as you make adjustments. You can do this with audio or MIDI sequencing.

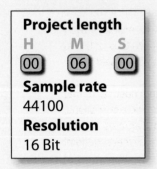

Check project settings
Set the length – for a four minute song, you don't want to scroll through 45 minutes of bars on screen. Setting basic parameters such as sample rate before you start can save a lot of difficulty later in the project.

Look at settings for when you open the application
Some software automatically opens the last project – bad news if there are multiple users in the same studio! The best opening option: 'Do nothing'.

Check MIDI preferences
There may be a MIDI filter which is stopping program changes or aftertouch. Certain types of tracks may be automatically created which you may wish to change. MIDI file import options are important too.

Listen for latency
All the processing in a computer can delay the passage of an audio signal. Make sure you have the correct and latest driver software for all your equipment. Keep your computer in top condition, with the minimum of extra processes running. Defragment your hard drive regularly.

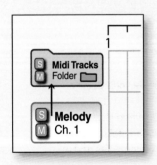

Use folder tracks
A large track count can make working on a project confusing. One solution is to pack some of the tracks away, out of sight in a folder. For example, all the MIDI tracks could be in one folder while you record audio tracks. You can mute them all with one click and open the folder when you need to work on them.

Learn keyboard shortcuts
Endlessly reaching for a mouse and clicking can really slow down your work.

There are shortcuts for most operations in music software. The number pad often includes all the functions of the transport bar. There are usually options for checking and resetting keyboard shortcuts in the application preferences.

PROJECT MANAGEMENT

Be professional in your approach

If you are submitting work for approval to clients, for exams or even just to your friends, make it look smart. Use printable CDs or labels and write some explanatory notes that are clear and well laid out.

Make sure written submissions are legible and neat, and that everything you send to others has your name on it. For examinations, clear labelling together with detailed logs and diagrams will not only gain extra marks but will also raise the examiner's general impression of your work.

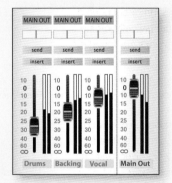

Save stems of your recordings and sequences

A stem is the stereo output of a group mix such as drums, backing vocals, keyboards, rhythm section.

If you save a handful of stems as stereo tracks, the piece can easily and quickly be remixed by you or a client without having to start again balancing every track.

For example, the vocal line may need to be adjusted for a video presentation – the stems can be loaded into a simple audio editor included in the multimedia software and be rebalanced.

Archive your work

When you've finished, go through everything on the computer or other media.
Make sure all software is labelled with project name and dates in a clear folder structure. Keep a separate copy stored safely in case you want to come back to it one day. Put all your written notes and a backup disc in a folder.

Make notes

Professional sound engineers make detailed notes about their work and this is helpful at any level. Track sheets, settings, equipment, microphones, problems that you encounter – all this information will help you work more efficiently and is essential for proper submission of exam work.

GLOSSARY

Alternating Current (AC): A flow of electricity that continually changes amplitude and direction. An audio signal is an example of an alternating current.

Amplify: To increase the strength of an audio signal (opposite of **Attenuate**).

Amplitude: The strength of an audio signal. When the signal is turned into sound waves by a loudspeaker, the amplitude is related to volume.

Attenuate: To reduce the strength of an audio signal (opposite of **Amplify**).

Audio interface: A device enabling analog audio equipment to connect to a computer, consisting of analog-to-digital and digital-to-analog converters.

Balanced: A type of connection or cable with two signal wires and a separate earth (ground) wire. This helps to cancel out interference and avoids having one side of the signal connected to earth.

Bit depth: The number of binary digits used to represent each sample, also known as resolution. CD audio uses a resolution of 16 bits. Higher bit depths are sometimes used in recording, which have to be reduced at the mastering stage (see **Dither**).

Cable: A bundle of wires wrapped in an outer sheath with a connector at each end. For example, a balanced microphone cable has three wires running between male and female XLR plugs (see **Lead**).

Capacitor: An electronic component that stores an electrical charge between two parallel plates. Only an alternating current can pass through it.

Capacitor microphone: A microphone in which the diaphragm forms one side of a capacitor. When the diaphragm vibrates, the stored charge in the capacitor is disturbed and an electrical current flows.

Compression: A process applied to an audio signal to control sudden peak levels. Example uses include evening out vocal performances and adding 'punch' to drum and bass tracks.

Connector: A plug or socket used to join cables to equipment.

Controls: There are two types of controls most commonly used in audio equipment: rotary and linear.

Rotary controls are turned and either have the minimum setting on the bottom left or top centre. As you turn one, sometimes you will feel it click into place at the zero point – this is called a **detent**. A Pan control is usually rotary and has 0 at the top, which centres the sound. A left or right turn of

the knob sends the sound in that direction. Volume controls usually have 0 on the bottom left, and to increase the signal the knob is turned clockwise.

A **Linear** control moves up or down. Sometimes known as a fader or slider, these have the minimum setting at the bottom and the maximum at the top.

Most controls adjust the setting of a variable resistor (see **Potentiometer**).

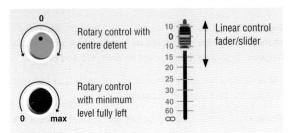

Cycle: An audio signal is an alternating current of electricity. One cycle is the change from zero to its highest voltage, then to its lowest voltage and back to zero again (see **Frequency, Hertz**).

Decibel (dB): The unit used for measuring the strength of a sound or audio signal.

Diaphragm: A very thin sheet of material which vibrates easily. Used as part of the mechanism which converts sound to electricity in a microphone.

DI box: A device that matches the audio signal from a guitar or other instrument to a microphone input on a mixer.

Digital Audio Workstation (DAW): A collection of audio equipment for recording based around computer software and an audio interface.

Direct Current (DC): A flow of electricity in one direction between positive and negative. For example in a torch where the electricity powers a light bulb.

Dither: A process applied to digital audio when bit depth is reduced, helping to reduce errors and to retain as much information as possible (see **Bit depth**).

Dynamic: In music, a dynamic is an indication of the relative loudness or softness of music.

Dynamic microphone: A dynamic microphone generates its own electrical signal by vibrating a coil of wire in a magnetic field.

Dynamic processing: Controlling signal levels using software or hardware such as a compressor (see **Compression**).

Effects unit: A device that adds reverb or other effects to an audio signal which is then mixed back in with the original sound.

Effected: A sound signal that has had one or more effects applied to it.

Electromagnet: An electromagnet is created whenever an electrical current flows through a wire. If the wire is coiled and wound around a metallic material the magnetic field is strengthened. Loudspeakers and microphones use electromagnetic effects to convert sound to electricity and back again.

Equalisation (EQ): The process of filtering, amplifying or attenuating a range of frequencies in an audio signal. Usually in ranges of frequency (bands) such as Bass, Mid and High.

Fader: A linear or rotary control, most commonly found on a mixer to adjust the volume of each channel.

Foldback: A signal sent to monitors on stage or headphones in a studio to enable performers to hear themselves and other pre-recorded or live signals.

Frequency: The number of cycles per second, either in a sound wave or electrical audio signal (see **Cycle, Hertz**).

Frequency response: The sensitivity of audio equipment (such as a microphone or loudspeaker) at different frequencies, often represented as a chart. A 'flat' response suggests a similar sensitivity across a range of frequencies.

Gain: A measure of amplification. For example, an amplifier may have a gain of 10, meaning that the output will be ten times stronger than the input. This is sometimes represented in decibels. Gain controls are commonly seen at the top of a mixer channel, controlling the channel preamplifier.

Hertz (Hz): A unit of frequency. One Hertz equals one cycle per second. It was named after scientist Heinrich Hertz (see **Cycle, Frequency**).

Impedance: The effective resistance of a circuit to an alternating current, measured in Ohms Ω (sometimes labelled 'Z'). Loudspeakers and the inputs and outputs of amplifiers are often labelled with an impedance value or simply Hi-Z (high impedance) or Low-Z (low impedance). An impedance mismatch will result in poor performance.

Insert point: A TRS socket on a hardware mixer channel. When a plug is inserted, the signal path is broken. The signal is sent out through one signal wire of the cable and returned through the other signal wire, cleverly using only one socket. It is mainly used to connect a compressor, which processes the entire signal.

Jack: A type of plug/connector with either a Tip and Sleeve (TS) or Tip, Ring and Sleeve (TRS). Commonly available in three sizes: 6mm (quarter inch), 3.5mm (mini-jack, often used on earphones) and 2.5mm (very small – used on personal audio players).

Lead: A commonly used alternative term for cable.

Loop: A section of digital audio recording that can be repeated. Often used to create drum tracks and backing tracks.

Loudspeaker: A device for converting audio signals into sound waves.

Mastering: The process of preparing a completed mix for distribution.

MIDI: **M**usical **I**nstrument **D**igital **I**nterface. A 'protocol' (set of agreed standards), that allows electronic instruments such as keyboards, controllers, computers and other electronic equipment to communicate, control and synchronise with each other.

Mixer: A device that combines and controls audio signals from other equipment.

Mixing: The process of balancing, panning, processing and adding effects to a number of live signals or recorded tracks.

Monitor: Equipment used to listen to live or recorded signals from a recorder or mixer. Also a loudspeaker with built-in amplification.

Mono: An abbreviation of 'monaural' meaning only one audio signal. With mono playback there is no sense of left to right placement of sounds. A small radio with one loudspeaker is an example of a mono device.

Multi-track recorder: A device that can record a number of audio inputs separately and play back some tracks while recording others.

Normalisation: The process used to increase the level of a digital recording. During normalisation, the computer processor finds the loudest samples and calculates the difference between them and the highest possible level. The difference is then added to all samples, bringing everything up as high as possible without peaking.

Pan: An abbreviation of 'panorama'. The apparent placement of sounds from left to right, usually achieved by distributing a signal between left and right loudspeakers (see **Stereo**).

Peak: 1. The highest level in a wave cycle.
    2. A digital signal which exceeds 0 dB resulting in a distorted sound (also known as 'clipping').

Phantom power: A DC voltage that is sent from a microphone socket on a mixer, preamp or other equipment to power a microphone or DI box. The phantom power is ignored by the audio circuitry.

Pick-up pattern: A circular chart showing the sensitivity of a micro-phone (when viewed from above) as a sound source is moved around it.

Plugin: Extra small programs loaded into powerful software packages to increase their functionality. There will often be a plugin folder in the installation folder. Effects and instruments are often added in this way.

Potentiometer: A variable resistor which limits the flow of an audio signal through it (comparable to a tap controlling the flow of water). Used for volume, pan, EQ and some other controls in mixers and other audio equipment. Also known as a 'pot', a potentiometer can be rotary or linear. For stereo signals, two potentiometers are mechanically linked ('ganged') together (see **Controls**).

Preamplifier (preamp): A small amplifier that brings a microphone signal up to a useable level at the highest possible quality. Also the first stage in a more complex amplification system.

Pre-Fade Listen (PFL): On a mixer channel, this switch cuts out the fader and sends the signal straight to the control room output. Used to set up the level of Gain for each channel.

Quantisation: In a MIDI sequencer, quantisation pulls notes towards a beat or other rhythmic division. This can be full or partial (so as not to sound too robotic) and can even follow a pattern or 'groove'.

Reverberation (reverb): An effect added to a signal which imitates the reflections of a sound from the space around it (e.g. a stage, room or cathedral). Most commonly used in mixing to bind tracks together and to control apparent front to back placement of the instruments.

Roll-off: A filter used to cut low or high frequencies. For example, some microphones have a roll-off switch to cut all signals below a certain frequency (e.g. 75 Hz) to reduce noise or 'rumble'. Named after the shape of the frequency response chart at the point where it 'rolls off'.

Sample/sample rate: There are two uses of the word 'sampling' in music technology.

1. The process of converting an analog audio signal to digital data – one sample is the smallest section of audio that is analysed. Sample rate refers to the number of samples per second. In CD quality audio the sample rate is 44,100 Hz (see **Bit depth**).
2. Recording an individual sound or a short section of some music.

Sequencer: A sequencer records and stores a series of MIDI messages and then plays them back to control an instrument. Both the instrument and the sequencer can be software or hardware.

Signal/audio signal: A flow of electrical current that represents a sound as it passes through audio equipment.

Sound module: A MIDI instrument that is played by a sequencer but does not have a keyboard and cannot be played directly.

Sound Pressure Level (SPL): Very loud sounds produce high levels of air pressure and can damage equipment and hearing. For example, a sensitive microphone could be damaged by the high SPL from a kick drum.

Stereo: An abbreviation of 'stereophonic'. A sound reproduction technique using two loudspeakers to create the effect of left and right placement of individual sounds.

Synthesiser: An electronic instrument used to imitate the sounds of real instruments or to create new timbres.

Tape: A recording medium consisting of stripes (tracks) of magnetically sensitive material on a reel of plastic or metal tape. As an audio signal is applied from an electromagnetic tape head, the magnetic state of the track is altered. They are used in tape and cassette recorders. Until digital recording became possible, multi-track tape machines were the standard equipment in studios.

Tracking: The process of recording individual instruments for a multi-track production.

Transistor: An electronic component which amplifies an audio signal.

Trough: The lowest level in a wave cycle.

Unbalanced: A type of connection or cable with two signal wires only, one of which is also connected to earth (ground).

Watt (W): A unit of power. Most commonly used in audio to represent levels of amplification or power handling capacity of loudspeakers. Named after James Watt, the steam engine pioneer.

Wave/waveform: A graphical representation of an audio signal showing changes in amplitude and frequency. Audio software will display the waveform of a signal and allow it to be edited.

XLR: A connector used for microphones or other audio signals, most commonly with three pins although some have more or less. The name is derived from the labelling by the original manufacturer and has no relevance to the configuration of the connections.

INDEX

THE AUTHOR

Mortimer Rhind-Tutt began his musical career as an orchestral trumpet player after studying at the Royal Academy of Music. He moved full time into education as principal of Ealing Junior Music School and is now head of music technology at Millfield School in Somerset.

▶ ACKNOWLEDGEMENTS

The author would like to thank the Rhinegold editorial and design team for their invaluable help in the preparation of this book.

The author has contributed to the illustrations and photography that appear in this book.